Global World of Shakespeare

Global World of Shakespeare

Translations, Adaptations, Transformations

Edited by

Abha Singh

Prestige Books International
Delhi : Sydney

Published by
Prestige Books International
New Delhi 110060
email: prestigebooks@gmail.com

Associate Office
P.O. Box 2250, Sydney 2001

ISBN: 978-93-82186-62-5

Printed in India

Dedicated

To my loving children

Major Rahul, Ragini, little Rudra

'You'll always be my jewels, source of pride,

No matter where you go'

From

the rhythm of the mother's love

Shakespeare

Others abide our question. Thou art free.
We ask and ask—Thou smilest and art still,
Out-topping knowledge. For the loftiest hill,
Who to the stars uncrowns his majesty

Matthew Arnold

Contents

Preface **11**

Introduction:
Remapping Shakespeare's Adaptations in Globalised Culture
Abha Singh 18

Bridging Cultural and Historical Gaps: How Appropriate is Appropriation?
Rajna Koska 38

***Otelo da Mangueira*:**
A Brazilian Shakespeare Adaptation in Musical Version
Celia Arns de Miranda 54

Text, Performance and Film:
An Intermedial Reading of Antunes Filho's *Throne of Blood/Macbeth*
Liana de Camargo Leao and Mail Marques de Azevedo 69

[In]Fidelity in Translation: Shakespeare in Argentina
Miguel A. Montezanti 89

Mr. Goodwill in "Rancho Grande," Investigating the 'Ghostly' Presence of Shakespeare in Mexican Cinema
Alfredo Michel Modenessi 103

Prospero's Books:
An Intermediate Reading of Shakespeare's *The Tempest*
Maria Luiza Guarnieri Atik and Celia Guimaraes Helene 122

The Stage as a Page and the Stage as a Screen:
Shakespearean Metamorphosis in
Stefan Pucher's *The Tempest*
Aneta Mancewicz 137

Celebration of Colonial Practices in
The Tempest
Chinnadevi Singadi 145

***Romeo and Juliet*:**
A Tragedy Retold in the Shanty Towns of Rio
Elizabeth S. Ramos 152

The Beauty, the Beast and the Sacred:
Re-Reading Desdemona, Lavinia and Ophelia
Cristiane Busato Smith 162

Shakespeare and the Culture of Innovation
C.N. Ajit 173

Shakespearean *Mahabharata*:
***A Midsummer Night's Dream* as**
***Pramilarjuniyam* in Kannada**
Sakshi Soni and T.S. Satyanath 178

Shakespeare's *Romeo and Juliet*:
A Study in the Light of Sufism
Abhay Leonard Ekka 132

Shakespeare in Indian Popular Culture:
A Critique of the Film *Omkara*
Deepak Kumar Rai 201

Rethinking Shakespeare in Hindi and Bhojpuri Literature
Abha Singh 207

Shakespeare in Indian Theatres
Bhaskar Roy Barman 224

A Comparative Study of Auchitya Theory
with special reference to Shakespeare's *Othello* and *Macbeth*
Rakhi Jain 237

Preface

As Shakespeare turned 450 years on 23 April 2014, it was time to celebrate and commemorate his work and intellectual brilliance. Since the 19th century readers have wondered how William Shakespeare with his education at grammar school and mercantile roots could have written so knowledgeably and eloquently on subjects ranging from politics and law to medicine and falconry. In fact some critics have come to question the genuineness of the authorship of the plays. In the last few decades we have seen that authorship speculation has gained considerable attention, the credit goes to internet. There are several smaller groups who have established that Edward de Vere, the 17th Earl of Oxford (https://doubtaboutwill.org/) was the true author of the poems and plays attributed to Shakespeare. It is the right of any critic to hold a democratic inquiry. But the authorship question seems absurd. The elitist notion that the son of a tradesman could not have produced Shakespearean canon is dangerously snobbish.

Shakespeare's plays, though derived from English culture, are universally recognized and applauded by people all over the world. The multitude of varied characters opens the plays up to a wide range of culture-specific adaptations and interpretations. Rather the bard's plots and characters turn out to be malleable and capable of incorporation into local theatre traditions. C.S. Sisson writing about India in the 1920s expresses his view about localized Shakespeare: "we should rejoice that Shakespeare is here, not translated formally, not imitated but transplanted as a living organism."

All the articles in this book show the process of 'replaying' a Shakespearean performance. They show that the 'replaying' as concept, metaphor and process is central to the understanding of Shakespeare performance. It also examines these interfaces in aesthetic, theatrical, cultural and political terms. It also looks at subversion, hybridization, fusion of location, textual structure and makes the audiences/readers understand how widely different cultures negotiate such encounters and the implication of this worldwide replaying for a reassessment of Shakespeare's theatre. All these papers make us think about the complexity of borrowing between cultures and recognition. Sometimes the discussion of intercultural understanding puts us in dilemma of authenticity versus the difference. The articles in this book make visible and coherent the forces within and without which produce "other Shakespeare." W.B. Worthen, one of the more prolific commentators on the performance of Shakespeare despite his alertness to the inevitable dominance of the text, as also towards the radicalized and 'neo colonialist proclivities' of western theatre practice, concludes his elaborate discussion of "other Shakespeare."

Shakespeare's continuing passage across different genres, media, histories and geographies affects at each turn his cultural status and authority. Working with contemporary theories of adaptation or intersemiotic translation, these papers explore the negotiation and shifts of meaning involved in the process of cross-media transfer among drama, performance art, opera, kathakali dance, musical theatre, film, and television. Critics have challenged the notion of 'fidelity' with a variety of arguments. Each new incarnation or version or appropriation is a complex arena, whose deformations have potential life and meaning of their own. Each paper seeks to raise practical and theoretical issues related to cross media transformations, including the blurring of generic boundaries, hybridization, and exploration of new genres. These articles address Shakespeare's myriad adaptations, spinoffs, derivation and fragmentary allusions in contemporary media that have in some sense drifted free from anchorage in the master discourse of Shakespeare texts. Shakespeare's master text is seized upon and redirected to new political or cultural ends. The concept of appropriation has been extraordinarily productive both in terms of underwriting and reading of specific Shakespeare adaptation and in terms of legitimizing an emergent sub-discipline. The way Shakespeare is getting popular in recent years suggests that it is time to ask whether appropriation remains an adequate model for analyzing Shakespearean materials in modern media and in a postmodern context. What are the limits of the appropriative model for understanding Shakespeare's circulation and transformation in an age of digital media and multimodal content?

Rajna Koska in her research paper on "Bridging Cultural and Historical Gaps: How Appropriate is Appropriation?" analyzes how the trans-cultural transposition of a Shakespearean 'original' to a different cultural context is achieved by punctuating the performance with the use of three forms of inter-medial transactions: a) traditional folk music, instruments, song and dance; b) the human body; and c) translation. The paper examines the production of *3 Henry VI* performed by the National Theatre of Bitola at the Globe to Globe World Shakespeare Festival held in London in 2012, where Shakespeare's 37 plays were performed in 37 languages. The performance is discussed as a form of Shakespearean metamorphosis and cultural transaction.

Celia Arns de Miranda's paper presents a Musical Stage Adaptation directed by Dandel Herz "Otelo Da Mangueira." It is an ingenious transportation of Shakespeare's *Othello* to the traditional Brazilian universe of the Samba School whose pageants attract thousands of tourists from all over the world. This paper focuses on determining the interrelations between both genres, emphasizing those elements that came into the composition of the musical "Otelo De Mangueira"

Liana de Camargo Leao and Mail Marques de Azevedo in their paper "Text, Performance and Film: An Intermedial Reading of Antunes Filho's 'Throne of Blood'/ *Macbeth*." study the reference in Antunes Filho's staging of *Macbeth* to Kurosawa's film, primarily the use of filmic techniques having to do with details of setting, scenery, costumes and masks which stand in further intermedial relationship to the Japanese non-theatre.

Miguel A. Montezanti's paper illustrates the reception of some of the Shakespearean plays in Argentina. Part I is more general in that it focuses on the limitation imposed by the audience's moral taste upon the translator's choices in transferring "strong" or "obscene" items. Part II analyses examples in which two texts *Macbeth* and *Hamlet* have been heavily transformed.

Alfredo Michel Modenessi's paper deals with the presence of Shakespeare in Mexican drama. Shakespeare has never been a frequent source for Spanish-speaking cinema or television. No film has been made 'straight from Shakespeare regardless of genre or country.'

Maria Luiza Guarnieri and Celia Guimaraes Helene's paper "Prospero Books: An Intermedia Reading of Shakespeare's *The Tempest*" is about Prospero's Books (1999), a cinematographic recreation of Shakespeare's play *The Tempest* (1611). This paper shows the super-impositions of mosaic, enriched with elements of the semioses, media and hypermedia in the transposition of the Shakespeare play.

Chinnadevi Singadi in her article, "Celebration of Colonial Practices in *The Tempest*," argues that the play reflects the colonial practices adopted by the British in these times. She avers that the play makes sense when read in tandem with the history of colonialism.

Elizabeth S. Ramos in her paper brings into discussion adaptation of Lucia Murat's *Romeo and Juliet.* In 2007 the film Mare'-Nossa Historia de Amor (More's Love Story) was launched in Brazil. Lucia Murat's re-reading shifts the Shakespeare lovers to the Shanty towns of More in Riode Janeric in the 21st century involving the drama in the mantle of criminality, traffic dealing and urban violence so frequently found in Brazilian contemporary metropolitan areas.

Cristiane Busato Smith, in her article "The Beauty, the Beast and the Sacred: Re-Reading Desdemona, Lavinia and Ophelia," discusses about sacrifice whether religious or secular which is central to the history of civilization and sacrificial pattern.

C.N. Ajit in his article "Shakespeare and the Culture of Innovation" examines the mechanisms which over a long period of time have been utilized to motivate, execute and successfully monetize the two kinds of innovation. In the process he examines the art of converting 'unfelt' into 'felt' and the perspectives of 'Past influencing the Present' and of 'Truth following Fiction'. This exercise is mainly based on the examples drawn from the works of the Bard.

Sakshi Soni and T.S. Satyanath in their article "Shakespearean *Mahabharata*: *A Midsummer Night's Dream* as *Pramilarjuniyam* in Kannada" interrogate the structure and styles of classical (Kalidasa) and modern (Shakespeare) play in Kannada and suggest that the striking similarities in the stylistic and musical structure found in them are a consequence of a public sphere and audience sensibilities that are integral formation of modern theatre in India.

Abhay Leonard Ekka in his article discusses the play *Romeo and Juliet* by Shakespeare. How Shakespeare depicts some of the aspects of human emotions and passions like love, hatred, patience, impatience, forgiveness, vengeance etc. In this paper he analyses and concentrates on the nature of lovers and human relationship depicted in the play and how they become true "sufis."

Abha Singh in her paper explores Shakespeare's presence in most of the Indian languages especially in the early modern drama that ranges across a spectrum from close translation to more or less free adaptation. A different motif, rhythm, new lyrical form, with a new language and idiom to match brings Shakespeare closer to common Indians. It may not contain anything authentically Shakespearean but then it could not have been conceived had the author not been directly or indirectly influenced by Shakespeare. Her paper shows how a Shakespearean play provides an incentive to Hindi and Bhojpuri drama and also helps the Hindi stage to pass from the crude farcical theatre of the folk tradition to a more respectable stage with proper dramatic effect.

Bhaskar Roy Barman focuses on the long gap after 1920 until the late 1930s Bengali Theatre gradually broadening its audience who were clamouring for the social and political realities of the Indian masses to be shown on the stage. When Shakespeare's plays were revived around 1948 on Bengali Stage, the production smacked of the influence of contemporary social realities but the undeniable truth is that Shakespeare has not disappeared from the theatrical arena.

Rakhi Jain in her paper discusses how Shakespeare was introduced by missionaries in some parts of India in the early eighteenth century. It was with the opening of institutions like the Hindu College in Calcutta in 1817 that a systematic study of English literature began and Shakespeare was enshrined in classroom. So after covering such a long journey, he no more remains a stranger to Indian sensibility. As a Shakespearean scholar, she was surprised to find all the twenty-seven kinds of *Auchitya* theory in his plays. She concentrates only on one kind *Kalochit*, that is, propriety of time in two of his plays: *Othello* and *Macbeth*. In all his plays, Shakespeare creates an appropriate atmosphere and presents his characters and images according to the time he chooses for the action of the play.

Shakespeare has become an international phenomenon. All these articles by various scholars have been written in honour of Shakespeare to mark his 450th Birth Anniversary. The plays have been translated into dozens of languages and performed into worldwide art forms. The British Shakespeare community has warmly accepted it as a process of cross-fertilization. The articles in this book address Shakespeare's myriad adaptations, spinoffs, derivations and fragmentary allusions in contemporary media that have in some sense drifted free from anchorage in the master discourse of Shakespeare Text. What tension, affiliation or resonance exists between "local" and global modalities of Shakespeare appropriation? In these papers, writers have tried to address the paradoxical diminution of cultural influence.

I cannot close these prefatory remarks without thanking all those who supported me in the preparation of this project. In this context, I wish to thank all the scholars who have contributed papers to this volume. I was highly excited and inspired to meet all my international contributors at the 9th World Shakespeare Congress, Prague, Czech Republic. I record my gratitude to them for contributing their papers, especially for Indian scholars and students. Thanks to all my friends, colleagues and students who motivated me to enter into the World of Shakespeare. I owe my gratitude to the publishers, Prestige Books International, for bringing out the volume so expeditiously and elegantly. Last, but not the least, I am thankful to my family members for their constant support, love and patience.

Introduction: Re-Mapping Shakespeare's Adaptations in Globalized Culture

ABHA SINGH
Dyal Singh Eve. College, University of Delhi

Shakespeare studies have included in their ambit performance both on stage and screen. We are no longer caught in the virtuosity of the playscript and the ephemerality of the performance. By combining text and performance, we open the possibilities of other definitions of literature. Bharat in *Natya Shastra* concentrates on performance and through it he focuses on the evocation of emotional responses. Aristotle in *Poetics* establishes the inter-connection between different art forms. There are many others who have stressed this every now and then through their medium—words, color, stone, and clay—from one art to another in more ways than one. Each art form chooses for itself different mediums and different ways of producing meaning. Literature depends mainly on words but makes use of method like sound, rhythm and form. Films work out in their own specific medium with the camera eye using language, music, perspective, space, composition, sequence and the human body.

One thing which is common to most art forms is narrative—this constitutes the impulse and the meaning. Another commonality is its semiotics which sends out clues for interpretation. When visualizing on reading the differences between the two mediums in their ways of expression and our own way of evaluation, films, theatre, literature all are product of culture; now the question is how we look at these mirrors that reflect us and at the same time shape us?

Re-Mapping Shakespeare

The Prefix 're' is used for repetition and reproduction that is essential to every engagement with Shakespeare. Whether it is an edition, performance or rewriting and transformation into different artistic and cultural form, for example, television, cinema, music, visual art, media. These kinds of reproduction may seem to be conservative but if the 'totem' is a Shakespearean essence, it can be valued for reproduction. Whenever Shakespeare is put into new form etc. geographical or cultural context, dual if not multiple authorship is involved.

Today's Shakespeare as a modern performance or as cultural text involves the audiences. Shakespeare's plays are affected by their environments as they are transposed into a variety of media, cultures and historical moment. Shakespeare is getting decentralized because of production of his plays where his name and plays are used as pretexts for cultural and ideological negotiation. The different geographical location of Shakespearean plays raises issues that transcend the individual performance studies and postcolonial studies; it also tackles theoretical issues of adaptation and genre in practical terms. Shakespeare today is reproduced in numerous performances that aspire to maintain fidelity to the author's intention.

Shakespeare's Work Travels

Shakespeare's greatness and pre-eminence as a dramatist is universally recognized. It is universally accepted that Shakespeare is not of one age but of all ages, not of one country but of all countries. Though his plays were written more than four hundred years ago and reflect tastes, customs and transitions of Shakespeare's own age, they are as popular today as before. They have been translated into almost all the important languages of the world and most of them have been filmed and staged through different media.

Shakespeare's work first travelled to India on board an East India Company Voyage in 1607. Shakespeare arrived in New Zealand and Australia some 160 years later in 1769 on another British Voyage of imperial exploration (Houlaham: 489). Apart from North America Shakespeare was being performed in West Indies, Australia, New Zealand, Japan, African colonies also. In India Shakespeare established its place before these countries. The diverse incursion of his work into virtually every culture is as much a part of his essence as in the English Shakespeare of Stratford. Local performances open the route to interrogations of the colonizing force of Shakespeare within this 'native culture' but also provide means by which the Shakespearean text is transposed in the service of a project to illuminate the social and political forces at work. Shakespeare as peace ambassador for the new world order is enacted in the controversial policy. To look for Shakespeare in the Indian cinema may evoke suspicions of bardolatory or even seem like a colonial throw back. Shakespeare was a leaven to the initial growth of Hindi cinema and has since nourished it in diverse forms, legitimate and illegitimate, as appropriations, recreations, relocations, and as 'after life' or presence. To trace this varied use of Shakespeare in the Hindi film is not just to navigate the changing attitudes to the colonial bard, but more crucially, to chart the shifts in the politics of intern centralism which provides another in road into the cultural imaginary of mainstream Indian cinema.

The only way of being 'faithful' to Shakespeare in the intercultural context is to relocate him fully. The reason why Shakespeare became more popular in India is that India is a country with diverse languages and literary culture that could assimilate Shakespeare in various ways. Shakespeare came to us at a moment when our society and culture were in need of new direction and change. Shakespeare in present young generation is understood to be with colonial hang-up. It leaves them free to approach Shakespeare in a fresh original manner. In 2004 Vishal Bhardwaj gave us *Maqbool* which was Shakespeare's *Macbeth* with *desi tadka*. Re-structuring the story around the underworld and its many deceits, *Maqbool* climbed quickly in popularity. One Shakespearean adaptation wasn't enough for Mr. Bhardwaj and two years later in 2006 he adapted *Othello* in *Omkara*. It was a super hit film. Even in Western countries a good number of film makers, novelists and playwrights have taken Shakespeare's plays and presented them in a different setting or with a twist.

The makers of Shakespearean films while fashioning theatrical raw materials into screen play have adopted various strategies as diverse as the impulses behind their various projects. Shakespeare's films are those which adopt as many features of a given play's structure and language as possible. While adapting them the maker of the film keeps in mind the accepted rules of mainstream cinema in editing, clarity of character and story and intelligibility of speech, understanding of relationship, and means of assessing more insight to the radical work. The most obvious difference between a screenplay and the text of an Elizabethan play is the number of spoken words—so in writing for the mainstream cinema, the dialogue should be kept to a minimum. Elizabethan dramatic text invites more latitude and adapters are more likely not only to abbreviate dialogue but to use it outside the framework provided by the original. Films however have their own non-verbal means of denoting transaction between characters. The modification of the text in a way is the unavoidable and regrettable consequence of filming. In a Shakespearean film the opening and the closing section should be shown in strategic manner so that it may not lose the essence and narrative shape of the original play. Cinema is expected to be more realistic, 'the big screen works like' the fourth wall 'on a naturalistic stage'. Shakespeare on films is means of generating popular interest for the bard. Shakespearean films encourage a director's appropriation of the play in a live performance.

Aim and Perspective

The present book proposes to examine Shakespeare's plays like *Macbeth*, *Othello* and many others. How the film adaptation took place, how the colonial subjects encounter modernity, though the parameter of modernity might be restricted. It will also discuss interaction between film and text and the cultural and historical context within which it is mobilized. What are the precise cultural capital which is being reflected in the film (*Macbeth*) *Maqbool* (2004) (Indian Film) by Vishal Bhardwaj or in (*Othello*) *Omkara* (Indian film). In fact the focus is to recontextualize Shakespeare in a globalised culture which might seem to require cartography. Cinematic texts have a life of their own, dealing as they do with the international market place of culture and communication. Both these films demonstrate not only a postcolonial play with Shakespeare's text, but also a confident postmodernist re-imaging of literary heritage, convincingly turning the war-torn Scotland of *Macbeth* into Mumbai's gangland. This book will also focus on cultural translation of Shakespeare in India for example *Macbeth* and *Othello*'s representation in *Kathak* and *Koodiyattam* form. Shakespeare's dramatic work occupies a strange and double-edged position in the Indian literary consciousness. On the one hand, it is a colonial text that the British imported to India as a tool to illustrate proper 'moral' behavior to their Indian subjects. On the other hand it has taken on a decidedly Indian identity, an identity marked by the postcolonial conditions of hybridist, subversion and negotiation. As a result the Shakespeare industry as it exists in contemporary India is a multifaceted and even contradictory institution. Indian director and scholars have appropriated and adapted the Shakespearean canon to suit their individual needs. In fusing the English texts with Indian concerns, both challenge colonial authority and articulate postcolonial realities. Today Shakespeare's plays serve as vehicles to investigate the realities of postcolonial existence.

Analysis of Shakespeare's film on *Macbeth*

There have been dozens of adaptations of *Macbeth* in gangland situation. A number of film makers have pursued analogies between Shakespeare's play and mob-crime drama. For example, Australian film *Macbeth* (2006) by Geoffrey Wright, *Joe Macbeth* directed by Ken Hughes (1955), *Men of Respect* (Directed by William Reilly 1991), *Maqbool* by Vishal Bhardwaj (2004).

These films show how Shakespeare is being retexualized by new hegemonic forms. These films are the postmodern representation of Shakespeare with its self referential system of echoes, illusion or even visual quotations. The extraordinary Bollywood crime epic *Maqbool* gives a detailed story of doomed forbidden love between Maqbool and his mob boss's mistress Nimmi with elements of the Macbeth narrative. In it, the witches' role (witches as a night club fortune teller in *Joe Macbeth*) is taken up by two comically corrupt cops who cast horoscope and manipulate lives to maintain a balance between criminal powers. The film's dream-like handling of the boss's murder provides one of the most memorable moments in recent Shakespearean films. An adaptation of Shakespeare's *Macbeth*, *Maqbool* is set in present-day Mumbai. It's a masterful creation, Bhardwaj has proved that Indians can make the best adaptation of the West, it's a visual gallery that is an intelligent blend of dark, tragic overtones and comic, satirical undertones, it is cinematically well conceptualized and executed. It is an Indianized version of Shakespeare's *Macbeth* in a different time and space. *Maqbool* is a path setter in many ways and is a winner in terms of its presentation and style. The fight is for self and not for society and this very approach makes this film look realistic and very contemporary though the basic idea of the film *Macbeth* is centuries old. Maqbool retains and even expands all the major relationships and events of Shakespeare's *Macbeth*, Duncan/Abbuji trust in *Macbeth/ Maqbool*, the prophesying witches/Cops who plant the seed of ambition, the seduction of Maqbool into treachery by Abbuji's mistress Nimmi, the killing of Abbuji in his sleep, the ensuing suspicion and fear, the poisoning of the bond with fellow captain/henchman. Banquo/ Kaka and his subsequent slaughter by Maqbool, the escape of his son Fleance/Gudden who survives to be the inheritor, the setting in of guilt and nemesis, the hallucinating Lady Macbeth, the beguiled Macbeth, the avenger Macduff/Boti and the tragic end—all these form the central structure of the film. After a basic transposition of the cultural milieu into a largely Muslim gang in Mumbai, there are consistent parallels with Shakespeare's text.

The cinematic visualization of the poetic images of the play can be found blended in the film. Unusual placement of Shakespeare's images accosts one at unexpected turn in the narrative, forcing at times a revelatory extension of meaning. These cinematic enactments though integral to the new narrative resonate fully with the old. A loud raucous chatter of crows and other birds, for instance, imagining Lady Macbeth's statement, 'the raven himself is hoarse that croaks the fatal entrance of Duncan under my battlements' (1.5.38) forms the background 'music' to Maqbool and Nimmi's first long scene, by the roadside, where she plants the seeds of treachery in his mind. The cawing of crow, in fact, becomes a choric comment on any talk of murder.

The festivity of the engagement party celebrations takes the place of the banquet in honour of Duncan, in the backdrop of which Macbeth and Lady Macbeth plot the murder. A huge steaming cauldron, that in the play is full of 'Double, double, toil and trouble, fire burn and cauldron bubble' (4.1.10-11) is glimpsed in the kebab maker's shop, where a rival gang gathers to plot further machinations of crime and revenge. The atmosphere of fear and terror unleashed by Macbeth, reflected in the lines, 'Each new morn/new widow howl' (4.3.4) is graphically picturized in Sameera's wild scream of anguish and hate when Maqbool pretends to commiserate with the break up of her engagement after Kaka's death and Guddu's flight. The dagger soliloquy is captured in a brief sequence in which Maqbool hallucinates that the blood of the goat butchered for the wedding feast has not been washed clean. The most effective illustration is of the central image of the play, 'Pity like a naked new born babe . . . Shall blow the horrid deed in every eye/that tears shall drown the wind' (1.7.21, 24, 25). This is visualized in Nimmi's newborn son, seen lovingly cradled by Guddu / Fleance and Sameera at the end, the very sight of which weakens Maqbool's blood lust, blowing his horrid deeds in his own eyes, making him drop the gun and walk out in a gesture of surrender, leaving the camera to mark a tear staining the glass visor through which Maqbool was looking at the babe. Pity as the naked baby remains the unborn child in the play *Macbeth*, emphasizing the sterility of the Macbeth. In the film the child is born of premature labour; it is also a visualization of the child that was 'untimely ripped' 'from his mother's womb' (5.8 15-16). The figure who was forecast as the one which will vanquish Macbeth—finally, at the very end, in the play, Macbeth's head is cut off and brought on stage, a sign of the just desert for the 'butcher king'. In the film, Maqbool walks out of the hospital, having dropped his guns and is shot down by Macduff/Boti who happens to see him outside. But no blood is shown, instead the camera pans them, tilts its vision to ground level, cuts to a view of the sky above and then cuts back to a close up, framing only Maqbool's head as fallen and rolling on the ground. At last the camera swivels up to show a clear blue sky, heralding the closing mood of 'the time is free' (5.9.21). These scenes show the stroke of genius, a summation of the popular and postmodern blend and also such cinematic, visualization create a 're-textualization' of the source. The ambiguities of the text extended in the film compel the reader to think about the power politics of that time. Reality and unreality had been cleverly juggled around to make the audience doubt one's straight perceptions.

Analysis of Film on Shakespeare's *Othello*

A more polished and assured cinematic rendering of Shakespeare can be found in Oliver Parker's film *Othello* (1995) and also Bhardwaj's *Omkara* (2006). Both these films take the adaptive layering a stretch further. Both these films from two different countries map the transitions and the continuities, the filiations and the ruptures from the colonial to the postcolonial, as well as they grapple with the schisms, fissures and conflicts of the colonial state and later of the postcolonial nation state which is increasingly marked by the economic and cultural process of globalizations; the bitter local and ethnic conflicts have also been shown.

An award winning film by Jayaraja (1998) *Kaliyattam* is a film in which the relocation of *Othello* becomes a means to examine the circulation of power within class and class structures in rural Kerala. It uses the indigenous folk ritual theatre of *Theyyam*, its conventions and community, to foreground the key issue of racism in the play by transposing it on to the iniquities of the caste system. Fair and winsome Thamara/ Desdemona, a Brahman landlord's daughter, falls in love with Perumalayan/ Othello, a revered Theyyam master, but dark, bulky and pockmarked low caste. Their happiness is poisoned by Paniyan, the Iago figure, a junior Theyyam artist confined to the minor comic roles, who covets Perumalayam's skills and position. A third Theyyam artist, Kanthan Cassio favoured by Perumalayan, unfortunately cannot hold his drink during the wedding celebrations and is made the scapegoat by

Paniyan/Iago. Cheerma/Emilia, his wife, is persuaded to steal the handkerchief/consummation sheet which is used to stoke the fires of jealousy. Thus, despite the relocation into a completely different ambience, the film manages to incorporate most of Shakespeare's plot and dialogue quite closely. The film is promoted as an adaptation of William Shakespeare's *Othello* in its publicity handouts, but its skill and sophistication produce an unfamiliar take on a familiar myth, going beyond adaptation, or even relocation to create a critical re-interpretation of the original in postcolonial terms. It uses Shakespeare to examine and expose the tensions of contemporary Kerala society.

Omkara is a more polished and authentic cinematic rendering of Shakespeare in the Indian milieu, it retains most of the basic plot. Vishal Bhardwaj takes a few liberties and changes a few situations slightly from *Othello* but he does not alter the gist of the story.

The movie begins exactly where Shakespeare's text begins—a conversation between Langda Tyagi (Iago) and Rajan (Roderigo), who is on his way to marry Dolly (Desdemona). In Act I, scene I, Iago calls up her father, "Rouse him, make after him, poison his delight." In the film *Omkara*, Langda further tells Rajan that his chief Omkara (Othello) has abducted Dolly. Similar situations we find in *Othello* in Act I, Line 82, "even now, now, very now, old black ram is tapping your white ewe!" Dolly's father, advocate Raghunath Mishra (Brabantio), mostly referred in the movie as "Vakeel Saab" (lawyer) is furious and confronts Omi (Othello). He puts gun to Omi's head and demands the return of his daughter. Same action we find in Act I Line 60, where Brabantio says: "She is abused, stolen from and corrupted." Bhaisaab (Duke of Venice) intervenes and resolves the conflict by mentioning the current political conditions and prevents bloodshed. Still unconvinced, Vakeel Saab grieves to Bhaisaab, the next day. To bring the final solution to this issue, Dolly (Desdemona) is made to appear in front of her father and clarify that she eloped with Omi (Othello) rather than being abducted forcefully. Similar situation is found in Act I, scene III, line 250 where Desdemona admits, "I did love the moor to live with him." In *Omkara*, Dolly also tells the events of how she fell in love with Omkara. The father leaves feeling betrayed and ashamed. Similar lines are found in the text Act I, Line 251-264, where Desdemona says: "My heart subdued even to the very quality of my lord. I saw Othello's visage in his mind. And to his honours and his radiant parts." The rest of the story we find also follows the original, even though the setting has changed. Instead of a soldier in the Venetian Army, Omkara is a gangster working in the services of an Uttar Pradesh politician.

Bhaisaab is elected for Parliament and Omkara is promoted from Bahubali to the candidate for the upcoming state elections. Omkara prefers Kesar over Langda as his successor once he enters politics himself. Langda is disappointed with Omkara's poor judgement and feels jealous of Kesu, his younger less experienced, superior, and hatches a plot to avenge both his offenders. He first causes a violent brawl between Kesu and Rajju by taking advantage of Kesu's law threshold for alcohol. Such irresponsible behaviour of Kesu infuriates Omi who now starts having doubts over his decision.

On one hand, playing the role of a concerned friend Langda convinces Kesu to appeal to Dolly, Omi's lover and bride to be, to mollify Omi. On the other hand he starts to disrepute Dolly by implicating Kesu's visit to ask Dolly for her help as meeting in an illicit love affair between the two. A 'Kamarbandh' (in Shakespeare it is the handkerchief) carelessly dropped by Dolly and stolen by Langda's wife Indu (Emilia) which eventually reaches Billo (Bianca) as a gift from Kesu, plays an important part in the plot, as evidence of Dolly's infidelity.

During the climax, on the night of their wedding, Omi is convinced that Dolly and Kesu have been having an affair behind his back. In utter rage, he smothers his new wife to death.

Langda shoots Kesu with a silent approval from Omi. Kesu is hit with a bullet on his arm. Hearing gun shots and in shock, Indu enters the room where Omi is sitting next to Dolly's corpse in remorse. Indu notices the 'Kamarbandh' and mentions stealing it. They both understand the fatal misunderstanding and Langda as its root cause. In retribution, Indu slashes Langda's throat and Omi commits suicide. The film closes with Omi lying dead on the floor and Dolly's dead body swinging above him, while Kesu looks on.

The plot of *Othello* relies crucially on 'hearsay'; 'calling', 'telling', 'listening' are salient actions in a play which dramatized poisoning of the mind through whispering in the ear. Right at the start we are told by Othello how Desdemona would 'with a greedy ear/devour up my discourses (Act I, Sc 1, Line 149-150) of how 'telling my story (which) wished she had not heard' (Act 1, Sc 3, Line 161) becomes a story through which 'the bruised hand was pierced through the ear' (Act 1, Sc 3, Line 219). Desdemona pleads with the senators 'to my unfolding lend a gracious ear' (Act 1, Sc 3, Line 244) when she wishes to accompany Othello to Cyprus. Later Iago plots to 'abuse Othello's ear' (Act 1, Sc 3, Line 393) whilst Othello fears that Iago 'makes his ear/ as stranger to thy thoughts' (Act 3, Sc 3, Line 146-147). A critical communication via the 'ear' is captured in the film *Omkara* through the many uses of the mobile phone. Commercially this film has a definite market both in India as well as abroad because of the fantastic Shakespearean adaptation. In spite of its agricultural setting, Vishal Bhardwaj's *Omkara* is very Shakespearean to the core. Seen purely as an adaptation of the English bard's play, *Omkara* is a work of cinematic brilliance, translating and transforming with sentences the characters of Shakespeare's aggregation into the Indian scenario. The cultural difference troubles less in *Omkara.* It is in attempting this blend, a balancing of the 'global' (bard) with the recognizably 'local' (regional Indian) that takes *Omkara* a step further in the appropriative trajectory not only in reconfiguring local genre but it also projects strategically into an internationalism of the modern globalised Shakespeare. Indian adaptations of the film *Maqbool* and *Omkara* are positioned as a third generation postcolonial adaptation. Here it is neither ethnicity nor authenticity that is aimed at but, rather, a postcolonial maturity in contemporizing the universality of Shakespeare into our own current concerns. While *Omkara* domesticates Shakespeare, *Maqbool* rewrites him in Indian terms. There is a long and indeed unbroken history of Shakespeare's films in India—it starts with silent film but what makes the current period so interesting is the sheer variety of cinematic representation. This revival would be called a renewed form of cultural imperialism.

Shakespeare and Transnational Culture

Even on stage, there have been several successful adaptations of *Macbeth* and *Othello*, in our own indigenous theatre styles. All these adaptations in different countries and the Shakespearean encounter with non-English players and intellectuals indicates the variable dynamics of Shakespeare's hybrid representation. In Fanon's view the colonized subject is hybridized most powerfully by his attempt to mimic dominant culture (Parry 31).

For Bhabha, colonial identities are always hybrid and oscillating, never perfectly achieved and colonial authority is rendered ambivalent in the very process of being enforced. The *Kathakali Othello* was produced by the International Centre for Kathakali in New Delhi. It is a highly formal style of theatre which evolved at about the same time as Shakespeare drama. This 'story play' is a hybrid form that drew upon various earlier arts. Its dramatic principles are based upon Bharata's *Natya Shastra*, the encyclopedia of Indian dramaturgy and theatrical techniques which dates between 200 B.C. and A.D. 200. The

Kathakali Othello is crafted within centuries-old form that has only recently begun to become internationally visible. The *Kathakali Othello* inflects the Moor's agony in a different direction and erases the schisms to Shakespeare's play. The appropriate context for the Kathakali adaptation of Shakespeare is within indigenous performative and intellectual histories rather than in simply the colonial heritage of English literary texts in India. The *Kathakali Othello* is not anti-colonial nor does it engage overtly with contemporary discourses about community and identity though it does read contemporary fissures of gender, caste, religion and ethnicity. It is not interested in Shakespeare at all. Only the Shakespeareans in the audience are concerned with its transgressions, or cognizant of those moments in which it either improves upon the original or fails to do justice to it. Ania Loomba says that *the Kathakali Othello* obliges her to mark the ways in which it 'provincializes' Shakespeare (163). The notions of hybridity also acknowledge a clash of cultures, rather than merely the slipperiness of discourse.

The original Bombay theatre was established as far back as 1770 and European amateurs used to perform Shakespearian plays, as well as musical comedies, fares and pantomimes there. But Parsi stage was different from such theatres in Bombay or Calcutta: it enlarged its scope beyond the obviously colonial circle of Europeans which included Anglo-Indians, educated Indians and some plebian audience as well.

Dozens of companies sprang up across the country, all attaching the phrase 'Of Bombay' to their names and financed by Parsi businessmen who were theatre buffs. These theatres repeatedly performed Shakespeare which gave glimpse of colonial India. The Parsi theatre not only performed English plays but literally took over the material culture of European theatre in India.

Shakespeare was in constant repertory on the Parsi as well as the Marathi and Bengali stages. In the Marathi theatre, a distinct

'Shakespearean style' of action has been identified, as opposed to 'Sanskrit style'. (Desai: 8) In 1934 R.K. Yajnik listed over two hundred adaptations of Shakespeare in various languages, despite the fact that many playscripts were lost and surely many others were not known to him.

In Urdu, Shakespeare has been the most translated foreign author. An Urdu version of *Othello* by Najar Dehlvi performed by the Parsi Alfred Company in 1918, opens with Brabantio entertaining Othello with dance and music. Desdemona and Othello's courtship is depicted through songs. Roderigo and Iago sing a duet to awaken Brabantio and his kinsmen with the news that the 'peacock is in the house of the thief' or that Desdemona and Othello have eloped. During performances of *Macbeth*, which was one of the most popular productions on the Marathi stage, the audience literally showed great enthusiasm for the actor Balabhan Jog as Lady Macbeth in the sleep-walking scene. The Parsi theatre and the Bombay film could be said to have created the idea of a national audience, the concept of the 'national' in each case is different and its relationship to 'nationalism' is also constantly changing. The shifting place of Shakespeare within different performative spaces, indicate a range of considerations that emerge from the travels of Shakespeare abroad. Individually they also lead us to locate nuances of culture and politics.

Recently, "Hamara Shakespeare" by the Prakriti foundation in India gave three performances based on *Macbeth*, but each time it turned out to be a different experience. We might think that working on a too familiar and celebrated work, a Shakespearean play, could restrain the creative space. But director A.J. Santosh disagrees: "It is a story that the audience already knows and you don't have to follow the original narrative. It gives you the freedom to go deep into the elements that interest you more. You could express your experience of reading the play and this reinterpretation could be interesting"

(*The Hindu*, 17 March 2011). The opening play *Macbeth* (in Malayalam) by Santosh, stood out of its visual treatment. The motif of guilt-ridden and doomed souls trying to wash off the blood stains on their hands pervaded throughout.

Through surreal video clipping use of reflections and body movements, it explored the possibilities of the visual narrative. As the director puts it, the play tried to observe the interplay of fundamental human nature of concerns, desires and greed that don the stage of conscious and sub-conscious mind.

"Koodiyattam" by Margi Madhu in all was a cultural translation. The briefing at the beginning and the introduction to basic gestures helped even the first timers to understand the performance. "Nrupa Padha adhirodhim duskaram naasthi kinchit/ adhiga bharanambho Kashsatamevam nrupanam" (Becoming the king was not at all difficult/to protect the throne and the kingdom thus gained is the most difficult task). As the actor enacts these Sanskrit lines, the plight of Macbeth slowly unveils before the audience. The plot was translated into a Kerala scenario or rather the inherent cultural elements in the art form stood out. Macbeth's victory was celebrated with pomp, complete with an array of traditional instruments like Chenda, maddhalam, edekka, and thimila, and king Duncan was served a traditional Kerala feast by his host Macbeth. The part where Macbeth enjoys the percussion with the rhythmic movement of his body, the expressions of the host assuring the king to enjoy the feast and Macbeth's reaction when he has the vision of a dagger are commendable. Madhu comments on how to bring in a story from a different cultural background: "Conceptualizing the performance was not difficult. We could see that Macbeth also goes though the conflicts, fears, and temptations like any other ordinary person. It is a story that any one can relate to. In 'Kootiyattam' bhavam (gesture) is more important, not the story. What matters is how the artist approaches the text, Here the performance ends when Macbeth faints on seeing the

Birmingham woods approach him, we didn't go ahead to show his death. The perplexed and chaotic situation that Macbeth finds himself in is performed at length. Like this, we explore the area that could be illustrated beautifully. (*The Hindu*, 13 March 2011). Poetry, lyricisms, metaphor, imagery and symbolisms are the prominent features of Shakespeare's works and Indian classical dance also works with these elements.

Recently, four damper performers in Mumbai (India) had used primarily the idiom of Kathak, supported by live Indian folk and classical music with same fine singing by Nageen Tanvir. Set about to explore the many facets of Lady Macbeth, the play opens with four performers driven in different directions criss-crossing the stage coming together and dispersing repeatedly and a reflection of Lady Macbeth's inner strife. The sprinkling of Kathak becomes more pronounced as the performers prepare for the arrival of Duncan, this becomes the cue for familiar-celebratory scenes of dancing women and pirouettes borrowed from Kathak. The rising conflict and the drifting of Lady Macbeth towards her terrible decision and deed, her famed unsexing of her self is depicted using the language of dance, and viewers are treated to some attractive stage moments. An elaborate 'Shringaar' sequence is quite effectively switched from its altered context of a predatory murderer adorning herself for the kill.

When an implacable Lady Macbeth emerges after having overcome her conflicts, we are able to make some quite straight-forward connections to the cult of Shakti. All through this, there is plenty of scattering of marigolds, water, fire and indeed, red 'Kumkum' powder. In its best movements the production allows us to follow the duel which ravages Lady Macbeth's mind, their theatrical impact heightened with help from the distinctive language and symbolism of Kathak and a smattering of other classical dance forms.

Looking at Shakespeare through Kathak will yield some felicitous performance leads but such creative exploration also suggests risk-taking with the possibility of some unexpected subversive gains. There is a possibility that a cross genre production working across two cultures which does not take itself or the audience out of its comfort zone, can offer a pale and limited glimpse of the full shock of the art experience. So, it is clear that working across genres and cultures is a venture that needs to be fuelled by creative ambition, intelligence and courage.

In these transformations of Shakespeare we can glimpse radical changes in the relationship between the popular and high culture, the indigenous and the foreign, the original and its appropriations.

Shakespeare's continuing passage across different genres, media, histories and geographies affect at each turn his cultural states and authority, working with contemporary theories of adaptation and intersemiotic translation. These papers have tried to explore the negotiation and shifts of meaning involved in the process of cross media transfer among drama, performance art, opera, puppetry, musical theatre, film and television.

Each of these productions with its alternative title announces independence from Shakespeare's work and each of their devisers can be situated culturally, nationally and even linguistically outside of the Shakespearean theatrical mainstream. At the same time it shows how the past we construct is shot through with the present and how fragments from those pasts can seem to intrude and anachronistically into a later moment. Each medium has its own specific configuration, various resistances may manifest in the process of metamorphosis through act of mediation, interpretation, and repetition. Together we hope to investigate the migration of Shakespeare texts through a sequence of media, and to explore the changes in authority, resonance, and use the plays undergo along such a circuit.

Bibliography

Greetz, Clifford. *The Interpretation of Cultures*. London: Fontana Press, Harper Collins, 1993.

Barnes, Jonathan. "Rhetoric and Poeties," *The Cambridge Companion to Aristotle*, ed. Jonathan Barnes. Cambridge: CUP, 1995.

Jakobson, Roman "On Realism and Art," trans. Karol Magassy. *A Forum for Literary Art and Culture*, No. 9. www.centre for book culture org.

Houlaham, Mark. 'Shakespeare in New Zealand,' *Oxford Companion to New Zealand Literature*, ed. Roger Robinson and Nelson Wattie. Melbourne: OUP, 1998, p. 489.

Osborne, Laurie E. "Rethinking the Performance Editions Theatrical and Textual Production of Shakespeare," *Shakespeare: Theory and Performance*, ed. Janes C. Billman. London, Routledge, 1996, p. 169. http-www.sha.globe.

Bristol, Michacl D. *Bigtime Shakespeare.* Routledge, 1996, p. 13.

Holderness, Graham, *Radical Potential: Macbeth on Film*, New Casebooks, Macmillan, 1993, p. 15.

Taylor, Gray, "Re-inventing Shakespeare," pp. 298-372 and Terence Hawkes "Meaning by Shakespeare" (London, Routledge, 1992), pp. 141-53.

Mead, P. and M. Campwell ed. *Shakespeare's Books: Contemporary Cultural Politics and the Persistence of Empire*. Melbourne University Press, Melbourne, 1993.

Chatterjee, *The Nation and its Fragments*, pp. 17-19.

Desai, V.S. *Years of Glory, 1880-1920 in the Marathi Theatre*. Bombay, Popular Book Depot, 1961, pp. 8.

Yajnik, R.K. *The Indian Theatre, Its Origins and Its Later Developments under European Influence*. New York, E.P. Dutton, 1934.

Halio, Jay L. *Understanding Shakespeare's Play in Performance*, Manchester, 1988, pp. 29-30.

Shakespeare, William. *Macbeth*, ed. A.R. Braunmuller. Cambridge University Press, 1997.

_____. *Othello*, The Arden Shakespeare, ed. E.A.J. Honigman. 1944.

Bharata, *Natya Shastra*.

Bridging Cultural and Historical Gaps: How Appropriate is Appropriation?

RAJNA KOSKA
S.S. Cyril and Methodius University, Republic of Macedonia

At the time of the English Renaissance, the notion of 'original' barely existed. Playwrights freely borrowed their plots from well-known sources, including plots from available translations of ancient works as well as from existing English works. At this time, fear of rival companies 'stealing' a play if it were available in print meant scripts were only entered in the Stationers' Register for printing after audience interest in their performance had been exhausted. Moreover, playwrights often took their storylines from contemporary events and stories of crime and punishment.

In this process of adoption, 'original' plots were inevitably transformed, with many complex factors playing a part in their metamorphosis. Identifying and analyzing these factors is a key aspect of New Historicism / Cultural Materialism approaches to literature. Taking such an approach to the works of Shakespeare, for example, we may see in Richmond's final speech following his victory over Richard III a fine specimen of post-coup Tudor propaganda, while the theme of witchcraft and the apparition of eight kings seen by Macbeth might be interpreted as evidence that Shakespeare was fully aware of James I's obsession with witchcraft and the king's anxiety about the legitimacy of his succession. In the Henriad, it can be argued, we see the appropriation of a historical event—the victory of Henry VII over Richard III at Bosworth—for two purposes: to flatter

Elizabeth I by depicting the triumph of her grandfather, the founder of the Tudor dynasty, and to remind the audience and the monarchy of the dangers of dissent and strife and the threat of history repeating itself. Thus, it can be claimed that the chronicles of Raphael Holinshed and Edward Hall—the main sources for Shakespeare's history plays—have obviously undergone extensive transformation in their many re-contextualizations, metamorphosing through a process of evident mediation into playtexts rendered as modern-day theatrical productions, or at the level of textual explication, against the backdrop of current studies of their cultural, political, historical and social contexts. Tillyard's *The Elizabethan World Picture* speaks of the Elizabethan perception of the world as single and uniform, whereas postmodern cultural theory insists upon a plurality of perceptions. As a result, the field of Shakespearean studies has also been the subject of debate focused on the plurality of histories as they are presented in his chronicle plays—especially so since history = politics and vice versa.

It is perhaps symbolic that the title of one of Shakespeare's favourite sources was *Metamorphoses*—Ovid's narratives of transformation—while another favourite source was *The Mirror for Magistrates* with its narratives about the ghosts of fallen princes looking at their images in a mirror. However, mirrors can distort images and we often see in them what we want to see—the transformed self. Hamlet's instructions to the players "to hold as 'twere, the mirror up to nature" is only the ideal that is difficult to achieve.

In such a context, the performance of *3 Henry VI* by the National Theatre of Bitola of the Republic of Macedonia at the Globe to Globe World Shakespeare Festival provides us with an exceptionally intriguing body of material that calls for dissection, as it were, with the instruments offered by the concepts of metamorphosis, transformation, adaptation, appropriation and inter-medial transaction in its broadest sense of cultural exchange. The festival was held in London from 21 April to 9 June 2012 and involved 37 performances of 37 of Shakespeare's plays in 37 languages by 37 theatres from across the world.

We have referred above to Shakespeare's appropriation of existing sources and the fears of rival theatre companies about the 'stealing' of plays. In Shakespeare's case, this resulted in the editions of his plays known as the 'bad quartos'. And from Robert Greene's 1592 pamphlet *'A Groats-worth of Witte, Bought with a Million of Repentance'* we learn that "the only shake-scene in the country"—an "upstart crow" and "*Johannes factotum*"—believes he is "able to bombast out a blank verse" like the best of them. Greene himself paraphrases a line from *3 Henry VI*—the focus of this paper—by modifying the original line from "O tiger's heart wrapp'd in a woman's hide" to "Tiger's heart wrapp'd in a player's hide," thus appropriating the line to his own purposes. Moreover, he accuses Shakespeare of appropriating not only *their* inventions but also their fortune and fame. Fischlin and Fortier address the problem of naming the process of the adaptation of a literary work, providing a brief survey of different terms that have been in use: alterations, imitations, spinoffs, offshoots, reductions, emendations, adaptations, transformations. They speak of the term *appropriation* as a word which "suggests a hostile takeover, a seizure of authority over the original in a way that appeals to contemporary sensibilities steeped in politicized understanding of culture." Shakespeare, then, according to his contemporary Greene, resorted to imitation, produced spinoffs and carried out a hostile takeover.

In bridging the gap between the past and the present in terms of metamorphosis and inter-medial transactions concerning Shakespeare and "what he hath left us," his surviving signatures are highly appropriate specimens as a specific instance of a paratext:

From a deposition of 1612: *William Shaksper* From a Blackfriars deed of 1612: *William Shakspear* From a Blackfriars mortgage of 1612: *Wm Shakspea* From Shakespeare's will of 1615, p. 1: *William Shackspear* p. 2: *Willm. Shakspere* p. 3: *By me William Shakspeare*

These obviously different spellings by Shakespeare of his own name, let alone the different spellings of his name by other and later authors—such as Alexander Pope and Coleridge—speak to us in a highly metaphorical way of the concept of metamorphosis. Clearly the differences in Shakespeare's spellings of his own name should be attributed to the fact that spelling rules were not standardized and fixed in Shakespeare's time; however, it is also evident that the name metamorphosed over time, both diachronically and synchronically. Thus it serves as a metonymy of his overall output and of the process of metamorphosis his works have undergone over the centuries, just as the sources he turned to for his plots themselves were metamorphosed in his hands. His extant signatures are attached, quite symbolically, to documents related to various transactions in processes of mainly legal mediations—a court deposition, a deed, a mortgage, his last will and testament.

Fischlin and Fortier also examine the etymology of the term *adaptation*. The word comes from the Latin word meaning *to fit to a new context*, and the authors claim that adaptation is a process of recontextualization. The Bitola production of *3 Henry VI* certainly fitted Shakespeare's original to a new context, and the end result was more than a cultural recontextualization. For within the same Globe to Globe Festival, *1 Henry VI* was performed by the National Theatre of Serbia and *2 Henry VI* by the National Theatre of Albania. Thus the three parts were performed by the three Balkan countries which, as it has been noted, were not in conflict with one another during the bloodshed that occurred in the Balkans in the 1990s. Here we should not overlook the fact that *3 Henry VI* includes a highly significant scene in which a father mourns his son and a son mourns his father. The universal matrix of the brutality of war is carried across time and space. In this context it is appropriate to quote Tom Bird, the Festival Director of Globe to Globe: "As for the histories, despite expecting resistance in asking companies in Serbia, Albania and Macedonia to tackle the Henry VI trilogy between them, he [Dominic Dromgoole, Artistic Director] got a flood of enthusiasm back. . . . They wanted to show how they feel these plays reflect life in the Balkans so well." The apprehension and assumptions on the part of the organizers, who spoke of having expected resistance, are politically imbued. And rightly so, given the centuries-long fears prevalent in Balkan countries—whether justified or not we shall leave to the historians—that the 'Other' can and will, or already has, appropriated their history, identity, territory. And yet such apprehensions and assumptions remain, in essence, political. (As we have already said, history = politics and vice versa). Thus Shakespeare becomes "a complex network of discursive, cultural and historical practices, not all necessarily literary. These practices are associated, negotiated and mediated by Shakespeare's virtual cultural presence, whether as literary figure or as sublime touchstone against which cultural identity is measured, however problematically."

Fischlin and Fortier examine the etymology of the term *adaptation*. We would like to focus on the etymology of the terms *medium* and *mediate*. Etymological dictionaries define *medium* as a word which derives from the Latin for "intermediate agency, channel of communication" and *mediate* as Latin for "act as mediator." Since its very conception, theatre—as a phenomenon and a medium—has been (ab)used as an inter-mediate agency, channel of communication and mediator. Bridging cultural and historical gaps once again, the following two examples alone can testify to this use of the theatre. The first took place on the eve of the Earl of Essex

Rebellion, when Essex commissioned Shakespeare's company to perform *Richard II* as a warning to the royal subjects to beware of Elizabeth I as a monarch just as feeble and incompetent as Richard II. The second example is Tom Stoppard's *Dogg's Hamlet, Cahoot's Macbeth,* a modern re-reading and adoption/appropriation as a metatext of the two plays in the context of the Cold War and the suppression of Shakespearean theatre in Czechoslovakia—suppression that resulted in people performing abbreviated versions of Shakespeare's plays in private flats. Today, postmodern theoretical and critical approaches do not perceive Shakespeare and his canon as taboo. Shakespeare is no longer a cultural monument. On the contrary, 'Shakespeare' has become an object of commodification and the Coleridgean perception of him as a godhead has passed into history. In Christy Desnet's words, "Culture is not sacrosanct." The process termed *reworking already-existing cultural material* by contemporary literary theory takes a myriad of forms and involves an ever-growing number of inter-medial transactions.

Our discussion focuses on the production of *3 Henry VI* by the National Theatre of Bitola, directed by the American John Blondell, translated and staged on the occasion of the Globe to Globe World Shakespeare Festival within the matrix of the concepts of the media in the widest sense of the term and forms by means of which appropriation and Shakespearean transactions are performed, resulting in yet another Shakespearean metamorphosis. The use of musical instruments, dance, song and sound effects, as well as the concepts of the human body and translation as forms of inter-medial cultural transaction in this theatrical production are examined from the aspect of transculturation which, by definition (in the domain of sociology) involves the introduction of foreign elements into an established culture, while it has also been defined as "a process of cultural transformation marked by the influx of new culture elements and the loss or alteration of existing ones." In elaborating on this production, we must refer to Gerard Genette's concept of inter/transtextuality. One of the subtypes of this concept, *hypotextuality*, concerns "the relation between a text and a preceding 'hypotext'—a text or genre on which it is based but which it transforms, *modifies*, *elaborates* or *extends* (including parody, spoof, *sequel*, *translation*.)." In the case of the production of *3 Henry VI* at the Globe to Globe Festival, five elements definitely apply, although in different ways. In and of itself, the play *3 Henry VI* [the play or the performance seen as a 'text'] is a *sequel*; the playtext *extends* and *elaborates* the preceding "hypotext," i.e., the dramatized account of the War of the Roses continues; the production of *3 Henry VI* performed at the Globe is a *translation* of Shakespeare's original and *modifies* it by adopting it to the cultural context of the country of its origin by introducing traditional folk instruments, song and dance.

The play was performed on a bare Elizabethan stage with only a few props and the cast wearing modern costumes, mostly long purple coats. In *Shakespeare Our Contemporary*, Ian Kott claims that modern productions which make use of modern technological devices such as revolving stages and those which try to replicate the dramatic conventions of the time when the plays were written are both bound to fail. In this production the director fuses the two approaches: bare Elizabethan stage—modern costume—stylized moves and dance—actors in slow motion. For instance, Richard shoves the dead body of Henry VI in the hole under the trap door, an important element in the design of a typical Elizabethan theatre, now faithfully reproduced in the New Globe. In sharp contrast, Edward IV's newborn son is represented as a white rose carried in the arms of his parents; in an instance of dramatic irony, the infant/white rose is also held by Richard of Gloucester, the future Richard III. Thus we witness a fusion of the elements of typical Elizabethan dramatic convention and a postmodern metonymical concept of representation.

As Queen Elizabeth holds the infant/white rose in her arms, she sings a traditional elegiac Macedonian folk song 'Jano, mori' ('Hey, Jana.'). The same tune is heard when Edward Plantagenet appears as king. At this point we would like to draw attention to the Bulgarian film *Whose is This Song* (2003) directed by Adela Peeva, the recipient of numerous awards. The film was inspired by an occasion in Istanbul when the director was sitting with a Greek and a Serb and a Macedonian listening to a Turkish band playing a folk song. All of them, herself and the Turks included, claimed the folk song was "theirs." In the Balkans as a region, the folk music and dances of different peoples have influenced one another over the centuries in a variety of complex ways. In general terms it would certainly be inappropriate (and politically incorrect) to "appropriate" specific melodies or lyrics as "purely" Macedonian, Bosnian, Serbian, Bulgarian. . . . Thus, in the context of this particular production, we are referring to the folk dance and music as Macedonian without any such aspirations whatsoever. This "disclaimer" is important for the issue and concept of appropriation in general, since in the past (not necessarily prior, during or before the bloody conflict in the 1990s) several folk songs from countries in the region were the subject of heated debates in terms of their origin, with each side accusing the other of having "stolen" or "appropriated" them. Cultural heritage belongs to all of us and it belongs to today's world music, which is termed so for a reason and which in its essence is a product of cultural exchange that is trans-cultural. A case in point would be Goran Bregović's music for the award-winning French film *Queen Margot* and his 'Wedding and Funeral Band' which fuses folk music from across the Balkans, thus 'appropriating' it in the most positive sense of the word.

In one of the scenes, fishermen speak in the local dialect of a Macedonian lake region. During their performance we hear the folk song 'Biljana platno beleše' ('Bilyana is bleaching the linen by the lake'). This is a significant topicality since a virtual footnote would be needed to explain the cultural context from which it originates, while the native audience would have immediately identified the song as indicative of both the location and the context. As young Edward (the son of Margaret and Henry VI) leaves the stage, Henry VI appears on stage accompanied on the piano by the tune of the folk song 'More sokol pie voda na Vardarot' ('The hawk is drinking from the River Vardar'). Before the arrival of Clifford, the folk song 'Zajdi, zajdi, jasno sonce' ('Set, set, bright sun') is heard, accompanied by the drum and a choreographed performance. The entire production is punctuated by the sound of the drum played live. During Margaret's speech following her defeat, a traditional male dance known as 'Teškoto'('the Difficult One'), perhaps the most famous of traditional male folk dances, is danced by her son in a stylized manner. The dance metaphorically conveys the hardships of life, and her son is soon to be killed. In one of the most dramatically effective scenes of this production, Warwick, who is played by a woman wearing traditional stylized neckwear often seen as part of traditional female costumes and jewellery and a silver double clasp worn as waist ornament in female folk costumes, at one point takes off her purple long coat and, now as a woman, dances a stylized traditional female dance. Simultaneously, the action on stage is punctuated by the sound of war planes.

Here we should point out the well-known fact that theatre speaks to us in non-verbal language, too. Non-verbal theatrical language includes light effects, gestures, and sound effects. In this context we focus our attention on sound effects or, more specifically, on the use of instruments, music, dance and song. In Shakespeare's plays there are a number of notable instances where such effects play an important role. In *Twelfth Night*, Duke Orsino exclaims, "If music be the food of love, play on" (I.i), thus conveying his romanticized perception of love. The sounds of a raging storm accompany the curses of the raging

King Lear left all alone on the heath, thus reflecting the storm in his raging mind (III.ii). Lady Macbeth and Macbeth fail to interpret the knocking on the gate repeated four times which, in a non-verbal language, reminds them that outside of their evil microcosm there is yet another world; soon enough we learn that it is Macduff knocking on the drunken Porter's gate, and that the castle's gate is a Breughel-like Gate of Hell (II.ii). At the beginning we hear the witches: "A drum, a drum! Macbeth doth come!" (I.iii.30). This takes us to the role of the drum and drum-playing in the *3 Henry VI* performance at the Globe. It began with the entrance onto the stage, from the auditorium—from among "the groundlings"—of a musician playing the traditional Macedonian drum, hitting it in the rhythmic pattern of 7/8, highly irregular in an original way, omnipresent in Macedonian folk music and dance. Formally speaking, any drum is a membranophone; however, in each folk tradition and culture it takes different shapes and speaks many different languages. As a folk instrument, the Macedonian drum is customarily made of beech, walnut or chestnut wood, covered on both sides with the tanned hide of sheep or goat. In this production the drum was played by a musician and, highly significantly, carried and played by Edward Plantagenet at important points in the course of the action.

In a number of episodes of this production the drum and the piano are played together, always live. Thus in a highly metaphorical manner these two instruments are a medium through which two different cultural contexts, those of mediaeval England and of rural Macedonia, are blended in the context of the play's production, resulting in a trans-cultural appropriation whereby, in this particular production, east meets west and the rural meets the urban; for the piano is customarily associated with an urban setting while the drum is typically seen as a folk instrument played in a rural surrounding. Thus the drum becomes more than just a prop; it becomes, in the terms of T.S.

Eliot's theory, an 'objective correlative'. (By way of definition: "The only way of expressing emotion in the form of art is by finding an 'objective correlative'; in other words, a set of objects, a situation, a chain of events which shall be the formula of that particular emotion; such that when the external facts, which must terminate in sensory experience, are given, the emotion is immediately evoked.") Edward Plantagenet does not part from the drum during major events, including those that are not necessarily related to military feats. When Margaret begs him to kill her after her son has been murdered, Edward hits the drum once, producing a powerful dramatic effect. Both piano and drum accompany the performance of the elegiac folk song 'Žali goro, žali sestro' ('Grieve, forest! Grieve, my sister!') during one of the battles. The episode is a theatrically powerful moment: the rhythm gets faster and faster, ending in meticulously choreographed frantic movements. Warwick dances a traditional female dance while the bloody battle is going on, delivering his/ her speech on death and the insignificance of material possessions. In this folk song the theme is the transience of human life as opposed to eternal life in the natural world. Thus it becomes transformed into/appropriated as a trans-cultural *danse macabre* (Dance of Death; English), also known as Danse Macabre (French), Danza de la Muerte (Spanish), Danza Macabra (Italian), Dançada Morte (Portuguese), Totentanz (German), Dodendans (Dutch), Surmatants (Estonian), Dansa de la Mort (Catalan). It is an artistic rendition of the theme of the universality of death: no matter one's station in life, the Dance of Death unites us all. The universal medium of music and dance in its archetypal sense thus serves as an *instrument* by means of which the archetypal messages of life and death, the forces of Eros and Thanatos, are conveyed across cultures. The sound effects, traditional music, dance and songs in the Bitola production of *3 Henry VI* are not grafted onto Shakespeare's original but blend in naturally. Although sounding strange to the ear of the culturally "Other," they are an embodiment of cultural exchange and diversity, thus making possible a smooth transition from one cultural background to another, a smooth Shakespearean metamorphosis and inter-medial transaction.

The actor's body, obviously enough, is a powerful instrument on the theatrical stage. This is a complex theoretical subject: here we refer to it as a medium by means of which this particular production of *3 Henry VI* touches upon the issue of gender identity and recontextualization/re-reading of the theme of disguise or cross-dressing which, as a Renaissance dramatic convention, lies at the core of English Renaissance drama and is one of the focal points of postmodern critical theory. As already mentioned, the role of Warwick was played by a woman in the Bitola production, an actress who later in the play metamorphoses—gradually, and in a meticulously choreographed manner, exposes her true gender. Rivers, the brother of Queen Elizabeth, is homosexual, though whether overtly or covertly remains unclear. It is in the rendition of Warwick's role that we see room for the application of Judith Butler's theory of transgender, just as much as it is applicable in the dramatic convention of Renaissance theatrical disguise, the most notable instance of which is encountered in *As You Like It*, where disguise is fourfold—boy actor>female role>female disguised as male>female disguised as male to play female in order to cure Orlando's lovesickness. Nor should it be overlooked that the role of the French King Louis is also played by a woman in this production. As one theatre critic put it: "It was also interesting to watch the development of the female sex through these three" [*1,2,3 Henry VI*] male-dominated plays. In Part 1 the only woman, Joan of Arc, is but a cipher. By Part 3 the women are running the place, the Macedonian National Theatre of Bitola adding to this impression by changing Warwick's sex." Thus the metamorphosis of sex accompanies the metamorphosis of the text: trans-gender exchange accompanies trans-cultural exchange.

Finally, translation is an equally important aspect of the concept behind the Globe to Globe World Shakespeare Festival. Obviously, all participating countries had to face the task of translating their plays into their respective mother tongues (in cases when they had not been already translated). Translation is per se a medium and a means of mediation that inevitably involves appropriation and metamorphosis. It has been noted by critics that the myriad languages in which Shakespeare's 37 plays were performed at the Globe may have been perceived by the many spectators as merely a form of watching the "Other" (to use a term from the discourse of postcolonial criticism) and that the audience simply saw the plays performed "in a different language" with no subtitles and with only brief scene descriptions in English displayed on two electronic screens—the digital age mediated in the act of this Shakespearean transaction conducted through the theatrical medium. As Martin Esslin puts it, "all translation implies a degree of manipulation of the source text for a certain purpose." Fischlin and Fortier quote Michel Garneau's term "tradaptations," obviously meaning translation +/= adaptation. The final definition of translation comes from Salman Rushdie: "It is normally supposed that something always gets lost in translation. I cling obstinately to the notion that something can be gained." Translating Shakespeare involves yet another form of inter-medial transaction, and that is versification, i.e., blank verse or unrhymed iambic pentameter. Naturally, the approach, strategy and theory adopted depend on the respective language. Whether or not Shakespearean blank verse should be strictly transposed in the process of its translation is a matter of scholarly debate among translators of his work. Claims have been made that the rendition of his poetic discourse should faithfully adhere to the original meter and syllabic foot, while certain translators uphold the view that blank verse should be adapted to the natural rhythm of the language of translation—in this case Macedonian—and that the iambic foot should be replaced by the dactyl or the trochee as more appropriate to the natural rhythm of Macedonian. In both approaches, however, translation involves metamorphosing the Shakespearean discourse wherever the specific cultural and historical con/text of the original requires it.

In conclusion, we take the liberty of referring once again to Janus, the ancient Roman deity. In the text quoted, Janus is used as a metaphor for the process of translation and the two faces of a single text—the original and its translation. Let us apply it once again, this time in the context of Shakespeare's output and its inter-medial transactions. Janus is a deity of new beginnings and passages—of doors, gates and entrances. He has two faces, each looking in the opposite direction. By analogy, the Shakespearean 'original' and its re-reading and recontextualization, its transposition to a different culture regardless of the medium (any of the described above), also passes through the gates of re-creation in order to enter another, different dimension. In this process, too, just as in the process of literary translation, the 'original' and its re-creation, its metamorphosis, placed against the background of the given con/text, are like the two faces of Janus—seemingly looking in different directions. And, again, the objective should be to convince Janus to focus the gaze of his two faces in the same direction, towards the same focal point. As Ben Jonson puts it in his famed poem prefaced to the First Folio edition of Shakespeare's complete works of 1623, "To the Memory of My Beloved Master William Shakespeare, and What He Hath Left Us": "he who casts to write a living line, must sweat/ (Such as thine are) and strike the second heat/Upon the Muses' anvil; turn the same,/ And himself with it, that he thinks to frame." In our context, the key words are "the second heat" which occurs during the re-reading, recontextualization, cultural exchange and transaction regardless of the medium (in our case, the production of *3 Henry VI* by the National Theatre of Bitola for the Globe to Globe Festival), while the 'doer of the action' of necessity himself/herself (in our case, the director, the cast, even the theatre itself) undergoes a process of "turning" i.e., transaction and (ex)change—it metamorphosizes. It is a process during which, surely, the expression on the two faces of Janus changes, too.

Works Cited

Butler, Judith. *Gender Trouble*. London: Routledge, 2007.

Cuddon, J.A. *A Dictionary of Literary Terms*. London: Blackwell, 1998.

Desnet, Christy and Robert Sawyer. *Shakespeare and Appropriation*. London: Routledge, 1999.

Fischlin, Daniel, and Mark Fortier, eds. *Adaptations of Shakespeare: A Critical Anthology of Plays from the 17th Century to the Present*. London: Routledge, 2005.

Kennedy, Dennis. "Shakespeare Worldwide" in Margareta de Grazia & Stanley Wells, ed. *The Cambridge Companion to Shakespeare*. Cambridge: Cambridge University Press, 2011.

Kott, Ian. *Shakespeare Our Contemporary*. London: Methuen, 1967.

Koška, Rajna. „Чекајќи го вистинскиот збор: за преводот на *Доктор Фаустус* од Кристофер Марлоу" ("Waiting for the Right Word: On the Translation of Christopher Marlowe's *Doctor Faustus*"). Skopje: Kulturen život, 2012.

Tillyard, E.M. *The Elizabethan World Picture*. New York: Vintage, 1959.

Electronic Sources

Adolphe Habere, *Intertextuality in Theory and Practice* available in pdf format at http://leidykla.eu/fileadmin/Literatura/49-5/str6.pdf. http://users.aber.ac.uk/dgc/Documents/S4B/sem09.html rareautographcollection.com http://www.livescience.com/19445-restored-shakespeare-signature.html

Tom Bird at: http://www.telegraph.co.uk/culture/theatre/theatre-features/9186796/Globe-to-Globe-Festival-Shakespeare-in-37-languages.html http://www.merriam webster.com/dictionary/transculturation pesna.org http://www.theartsdesk.com/theatre/ globe-globe-henry-vi-parts-1-2-and-3-shakespeares-globe

Otelo da Mangueira A Brazilian Shakespeare Adaptation in Musical Version

CELIA ARNS DE MIRANDA

Otelo da Mangueira, a musical stage-adaptation directed by Daniel Herz, is an ingenious transposition of Shakespeare´s *Othello* to the traditional Brazilian universe of the Samba Schools whose pageants attract thousands of tourists from all over the world every year. Gustavo Gasparani, who is the writer of the performance text, has succeeded in metamorphosing the main characters of the Shakespearian plot into a dispute for consecrating the samba-song at *Morro da Mangueira*, Rio de Janeiro, during the carnival of 1940, which is the year samba was raised to the category of national rhythm. The dispute, just as in the Shakespearian plot, puts into evidence the extreme conflicts human relationships bear, oscillating between love and hatred, and becoming destructive when aggravated by intrigue and excessive passions.

Patrice Pavis (10) develops the theoretical assumption that considers the transposition or transformation of a work, from one genre to another as one of the possible forms of adaptation. According to the author, the adaptation keeps the narrative contents (with greater or lesser deviations), while the discursive structure is radically transformed, once there is the change to an entirely different enunciation device. While analysing *Otelo da Mangueira*, one can notice that during this semiotic operation of transference there was, on the one hand, the transformation of a tragedy into a musical theatre (genre change), and on the other hand, the passage of the dramatic text to the staging of the performance in itself. This paper will focus on determining the interrelations between both genres, emphasizing those elements that came into the composition of the musical *Otelo da Mangueira.*

Just as most musicals, *Otelo da Mangueira* is divided into two acts: the nineteen samba-songs in the musical are creations of several composers, such as Cartola, Arthurzinho, Ze Ramos, Geraldo Pereira, Elpídio dos Santos, Nelson Sargento, Zé com Fome, Hélio Cabral, Cícero dos Santos, Gustavo Gasparani and Chico Modesto, among others. Gasparani's text is a result of deep research about the composer's songs from Mangueira. This way, lyrics that speak of passions, jealousies and treason, telling the daily life and events of the local scoundrels, perfectly adapt to the countless situations in Shakespeare's plays. One of the aspects that will be analysed in this research is the use of sambas to write the screenplay, the way they were put to the theatrical event's service. When they are inserted into the dramatic text to serve specific purposes, those songs reach a dramatic function in the musical and help to tell the story.

As its own title suggests, there is no doubt that there is a visible approximation between Gasparani's musical *Otelo da Mangueira* and Shakespeare's *Othello.* Among the several equivalences that can be established between both texts, this paper will focus on the study of the discursive structures, that is, of the elements that make up the organization of the dramatic structure in both textual universes. This paper will make it possible to determine the function those sambas that compose the show *Otelo da Mangueira* assume in the development of the plot. As the place of a song in any musical is never arbitrary, there are moments, circumstances in the plot that demand the insertion of one. However, it is essential that the characters show the motives that made them express their feelings and emotions through music, otherwise these songs would be empty exercises. Musical interludes always express those feelings and/or concerns that characterize life—joy, sorrow, love, displeasure, indignation, regret, hatred, anger—when these feelings overflow, characters sing.

Although many successful musicals open with a few pages of dialogue before the opening number, audiences generally prefer when they start with music. When a musical is entirely sung or when songs are written especially for that musical, the opening number becomes a proper dramatic tool. In this case, at the end of the first song the audience will already have had access to the information that generally is contained in the exposition of the plot, such as, for instance, the place where the plot will develop, the type of characters that will be in it and which basic atmosphere will prevail.

A slightly diversified process occurs in *Otelo da Mangueira*, exemplifying another option for composing musical theatre, that is, when songs that were previously created are inserted into the dramatic action, in an effective way and being used for specific functions. In Gasparani's musical, the opening number (*Song 1;* 3) is the samba *Sala de Recepcao* (Reception-room), by Cartola1: although it does not introduce action itself, through the exposition of the characters' internal motivations and the insertion of other basic elements to set the plot, the opening song determines the tone for the rest of the musical, that may, or may not, be confirmed throughout the action. At the same time, it characterizes the Mangueira suburb, where the action will develop, as being inhabited by poor and simple people who have only the sun to heat them up. However, residents say that happiness lives in the suburb in which they dwell because they are all soothed by the pride of belonging to Mangueira, of being the first champions and that the other samba schools even cry because they envy the highlighted position Mangueira occupies.

This opening song is presented by Tia Fe who, throughout the performance, will consolidate her role as a community leader. It is important to notice that Tia Fe has the help of a chorus that is formed by people who live in the place. While the musical number is being performed and the rest of the actors play out the daily life in the community, a picture of the *Morro da Mangueira* in the 18th century–the time when it was still being formed–is projected. As the projection is concluded, the actors are illuminated and the show begins a few days before Rio de Janeiro's carnival in 1940. There is no doubt that this opening number complies with what John Kenrick (2000-2004; 7) considers an effective song, that is, one that produces the expected effect. According to Kenrick, a quality opening song establishes the tone of the show that is about to be presented. This must be the most impressive of the whole set of repertoire, as a great opening number affirms to the audience that other good songs will be part of the performance.

The school exaltation spirit that prevails in the opening number will be completely reversed as the plot unfolds. Very appropriately, the play starts with Dirceu—the character that corresponds to Shakespeare's Iago—opening the curtains. He is the actor-director character who manipulates the performance wickedly: text and scene are his. He takes every opportunity to assemble his intrigue network: he insinuates untruths, poisons ears and, pretending to be earnest, manages to manipulate situations in such a way that the other characters seem to be puppets in his hands. The final verses of the samba lyrics which are sung in the opening number, "Here we embrace the enemy // As if he were a brother" (3) express within the plot an ambivalence of meaning. These verses become the reverse of expectations as Dirceu, on the one hand, shows to be Otelo's worst foe and, on the other hand, as Otelo does not discern

Dirceu's real nature, he embraces him as if he were his brother and believes in his feigned insinuations.

In his *Shakespearian Tragedy*, H.B. Charlton (apud, Heliodora, 275) mentions, when referring to the Shakespearian *Othello:* "the tragedy stems from the marriage of two persons with vastly diverse origins and education." In *Otelo da Mangueira* the social differences of Otelo and Lucíola (Shakespeare's Desdemona) are also pointed out. Although Otelo is President and founder of the Mangueira Samba School and is renowned as a great composer, his marriage to Lucíola was not approved by her father. Lucíola is daughter to a famous tailor in São Cristóvão and she leaves her home and family to live with Otelo in the community. She is known for her beauty and grace when dancing, and became Mangueira's standard bearer. Furthermore, she is also the school President's wife. What becomes quite evident, right from the first scenes, is that Dirceu is aware of the socio-racial differences between Otelo and Lucíola, and makes use of this fact to articulate his purposes when he tries to attract Jurandir (a character that fits in the Shakespearean characterization of Roderigo), who is in love with Lucíola, to his intrigue games.

By the end of Act I, scene ii, Song 2 (10) is presented immediately after the audience is made aware that Otelo was awarded the title of 'Citizen of Samba': he brings in his hands the champion's crown. Everyone can see that the couple—Otelo and Lucíola—is at their utmost conjugal harmony and that Otelo has reached the position of admiration and respect from the dwellers of the community. It is significant that the samba *Eu quero é nota* (What I Want is Money) by composer Arthurzinho is started by Otelo. Next, Sabiá and Chicão, local residents, take over the vocals while Otelo makes an exhibition of his gifts as a dancer and musician. According to the songs classification, regarding the function they take in musicals, the stanza that Otelo sings can be considered an Expression Song, in which he sings of his simple origin and his desire to have more money so he may live in Leblon, but that, in fact, he is a mere worker, with no money and living in a humble shack in Mangueira. In this kind of song the character expresses his feelings through music: his fears, sorrows, dreams and purposes, thus allowing the audience to know him a bit better.

In musical-theatre, songs are often followed by live dances and live instrumental music, and this sends us back to the beginning of musicals, when they still had the main purpose of entertaining spectators by presenting nice songs and dances. That is why the samba Eu quero é nota (What I want is money) can also be considered as an Entertaining Song: while Chicão and Sabiá sing their stanzas, talking about the happy and peaceful life in the community, and of the subtleties of trickery, Otelo shows his skills as a dancer and player. It must also be mentioned that this musical has live instrumental music from beginning to end.

As the dramatic action develops, Dirceu, just as the Shakespearian Iago, reveals his masks, his true intentions and his perverse nature. Everything progresses as he had planned: in the tragedy Shakespeare wrote, as well as in Gasparani's musical, both characters, Iago//Dirceu, respectively, in one of the most striking soliloquies, not only disclose their wicked plans, but they also invoke the help of devilish forces to reach their purposes: in *Othello* by Shakespeare, Iago mentions: "it is engender'd:—hell and night // Must bring this monstrous birth to the world's light" (i, iii, 1120); in Otelo da Mangueira, Dirceu emphasizes that he "knows that Otelo is going to listen to me. It´s not going to be difficult to convince him . . . he would put his head in the mouth of a lion for me. . . (Laughs). And as long as he isn't beaten . . . I'll push him to the abyss like an old goat. May Exu and darkness guide me!" (16)

It becomes extremely interesting and necessary to notice that the musical *Otelo da Mangueira* includes several aspects that partake of the Afro-Brazilian traditions of the cults to the *orixás* (African gods). The absorption of Afro-Brazilian elements by Gasparani in this musical points out the cultural assimilation that happened in colonial Brazil through religious syncretism, which is ascribed to African slaves meeting Catholicism. The most significant reference that occurs in the musical is when Dirceu invokes the Exu entity (see the previous quotation), which is commonly acknowledged as a devilish figure. Anthropologist Rita Laura Segato states:

> Exu is seen as a very powerful and ubiquitous *orixa* that uses means that are often described as mischievous and deceiving, although not in an exclusive manner, to interfere in the relations between gods and persons. That is why it is said that a person is acting as an Exu in a particular situation if the outcome of his intervention between two or more people looks as if the purposes were arguable or the consequences are negative for the relationship of the people involved. (75)

Within this context it can be observed as made clear by Iago's words previously included, that Shakespeare's *Othello*, the source text for the musical *Otelo da Mangueira*–also includes, not only a speech that is related to diabolic actions which reveal a harshness of intentions, but also puts "into action a mechanism of wickedness, envy and stupidity" (Kott, 111) through Iago's implacable and diabolic guidance. The intensity of hatred Iago has for Othello is emphasized from his first words, when his vile, selfish and ill-tempered character is revealed, which makes use of any means for self-promotion: "I follow him to serve my turn upon him: . . . In following him I follow but myself; // Heaven is my judge, not I for love and duty, // But seeming so for my peculiar end: // I am not what I am." (I, i, 1113-14). Othello is dragged down by this honest-faced villain and taken to a dead end: he reaches the bottom of the dark and obscure pit of human experience that is exposed by his "Farewell" discourse, by the pact the protagonist and villain perform knelt down (III, iii) and by his passing out (IV, i) that represents his own fall and his complete submission to Iago's powers. From the moment Othello comes to believe in Iago's insinuations, he completely loses his perception of reality and chaos comes to Cyprus. Othello absorbs Iago's obsessions and will borrow his voice when, for instance, he transforms Desdemona into a devil: "Heaven truly knows that thou art false as hell" (IV, ii, 1140). A few lines further on, Othello once again gives signs of his mental confusion and of the unbearable stress that takes hold of him when he mentions "heaven" in the first verse of a long speech that ends with the word "hell" (IV, ii, 55-72, 1140-41). At this moment he is making another allusion to Desdemona's infidelity when he suggests that her angel's rosy lips would become as repulsive as hell. Emilia, in turn, becomes to Othello's eyes the doorkeeper of hell, the place where Desdemona betrays him: "Some of your function, mistress; // Leave procreants alone, and shut the door; // Cough, or cry hem, if any body come." (IV. ii., 1140)

In the musical *Otelo da Mangueira*, it can be noticed that Dirceu fits even more perfectly the description of the characteristics and methods used by the entity Exu, as exposed by Segato: he is the self-seeking, ambitious, selfish antagonist that feels duplicate pleasure in the unbearable suffering he is able to inflict on Otelo, becoming the pivot of the couple's tragic end. He shows himself to be an unscrupulous envious being, having mean intentions and an ill-tempered character. He boasts that God "invented him to the Devil's despair" and that he made "of samba the cathedral of hell" (36). Everything progresses as Dirceu had planned: after Candinho is discharged from his position as harmony director at the school, Dirceu suggests that the lad should appeal to Lucíola in order to recover his position. In fact, what Dirceu needed was a subterfuge so he could parallel Lucíola's fidelity to Otelo's eyes. He states: "Several are the faces of the devil! This wolf's here disguised as good coun'slor.

While you trouble Lucíola to fix your blunders I'll whisper into Otelo's ears some pestilent ideas about our flag standard." (28) In Act I, scene 9, the spectators have an opportunity to observe Dirceu cunningly attract Otelo to the trap of intrigue: he insinuates, instigates, poisons, distorts facts, manipulates words and by the end of this scene he is absolutely sure he has managed to instil doubt into Otelo's mind, making him totally confused with respect to the facts (32-36). He has the nerve to warn Otelo to be careful because "jealousy is a monster that enters our bodies and corrodes all that it meets." (35)

In scene 10 (Act 1), which immediately follows the previous context, Dirceu is fully aware that Otelo is in his hands: "the seed has been planted"; now, as he reveals, he "must be patient and await for the evil to spread" (36). Next, there is the impression that he invokes malefic forces when he recites some verses from a samba by Cartola: "God invented me for the Devil's despair. // I made of samba the cathedral of hell. // Mad, raving mad, insane. // I've been doing of my life whatever I want." (36) Next, he sings Song 8 (37), Lei do cão (The Dog's Law), by Nelson Sargento, which is a perfect description of the plot's present situation in which the war between Dirceu and Otelo is declared, even if Otelo is not yet aware of the fact: "it's an eye for an eye, a tooth for a tooth // I make no options // War is war" (37). As in a soliloquy, Dirceu lets his mask fall and reveals who he truly is: "I've torn my fool's award // I'm no longer a lamb, now I'm a wolf // . . . It's dog's law // It's harshness // No softness // To no one // First me // Second me // Third and fourth, also me // . . . Behaving like this I live very well" (37). One can notice that this song fits perfectly, not only to the development of the plot, but also to the character's construction. According to the songs' classification, regarding the function they take throughout the plot, this one can be considered, on the one hand, as an Expression Song, as Dirceu, by means of the music, fully assumes his identity as a selfish, envious, diabolic and self-seeking person and, on the other hand, it can also be considered as a Decision Song because Dirceu uses the song to reflect on his positions and, finally and definitively, assumes his plans.

On the night of carnival pageants, while everyone is busy with the last and final details, Otelo enters the shack, visibly troubled. Everyone notices that he is physically transfigured and acting in an abrupt and deranged manner, as he becomes impatient with everyone and acrimonious with Lucíola. He reveals the suffering, disillusion, sorrows and inner conflict that overcome him and that are annihilating the peace in his soul, with a soliloquy that was made from several sambas:

> Insomnia makes me mad, makes my nights a torture. My sad figure is the picture of disillusion. Ingratitude hurts inside. . . . I didn't deserve it. To suffer is my condemnation! And to soften this pain, only death. I've looked for fortune and didn't find it. Oh Lord! Pity me! I cannot live like this. . . . I've no more pleasure in gazing at the moonlight through the holes in my shed's roof and it's not a charming palace, anymore, 'cause I'm hurt and wounded in my heart. If love is this that I found, I'll never love again. Why did I marry? What for? (41)

There are no doubts that this mixture of several sambas can also be considered as an Expression Song, due to the highly subjective, emotional and almost confessional contents of the text. Gasparani presents a photograph of Otelo's soul, magnificently extracted from different sources, offering us an excellent opportunity to observe how good results may be reached from textual and inter-genre dialogisms.

After the conflict is intensified, one of the moments in which the crisis reaches its peak in the development of the dramatic structure, in both Shakespeare's *Othello* and the musical, is when both hero and villain, knelt, establish a pact. Upon analysing the formal structure of *Otelo da Mangueira*, this critical moment in the plot ends the first act of the play with a song, which is most appropriate, once a musical must always end the first act in a point of suspense, in a point that is essential to the plot so that the spectators are still motivated for the beginning of the second act. Song 10 (44), Deus, Onipotente Criador (God, Omnipotent Creator) by composer Cícero Santos, which is sung jointly by both Dirceu and Otelo, expresses how much Otelo is feeling that he is a victim of the whole situation that Dirceu is artfully preparing. In this Expression Song Otelo asks God to be merciful because he has not had one minute of peace and also for his pain to be mitigated. The great irony is that at this very moment Otelo is establishing a pact with Dirceu, the one who is causing all this suffering.

The music that starts the second act must musically express a totally new rhythm in relation to all that has been presented previously; to present something new has the purpose of keeping the musical quality and also to draw the spectators' attention and keep them motivated to keep their attention focused on the unfolding of the dramatic action. After the joyful *pout-pourri* of exaltation to Mangueira (Song 13; 45) which is sung by the samba school's women from the community during the opening of Act 2, Otelo and Lucíola have an argument because she cannot find the handkerchief he had given her as a gift. Otelo's words, when he says that this handkerchief "is as precious as his own life" and that according to his mother "To lose or give the handkerchief to someone certainly [would mean] a curse" (47), are a torture to Lucíola and an anticipation of the tragic events. It is very significant that by the end of this harsh exchange of words in which Otelo demonstrates all his resentment, disillusion, sorrow, making evident his visible emotional decay by using sordid and cruel words when referring to Lucíola, they split up, one to each side, to sing in duet Song 14 (51), Luz Negra (Black Light), by Nelson Cavaquinho and Amâncio Cardoso, and Humming-Bird (Beija-Flor) by Nelson Cavaquinho, Noel Silva and Augusto Tomás Júnior. This physical separation in the beginning of the duet brings a scenic result that is quite appropriate, once after this song is finished, the couple will definitely part until the tragic end occurs. In the song's introduction, Otelo recites part of the poem Restos mortais (Mortal Remains), by Carlos Cachaça, which shows how much he is entangled by the destructive game that Dirceu prepared:

> From your fake love little is left for me. It was the inebriety of the party and the pleasure. It was like the poison that horribly harms and someone innocent drinks without knowing. But even without wanting I'll keep forever, in my poor mouth, the displeasure, so much bitterness of a kiss you gave, false, nebulous, rough, mortal remains of your dreadful love. (51)

This duet is a Transition Song because it is connected with a moment of change, or conversion in the couple´s relationship, which is definitely going to reflect in the dramatic action. The fact that Otelo and Lucíola sing the first three stanzas separately and the last one together becomes especially representative of this critical moment: what is being expressed through the last verses of the duet becomes a prediction of what is going to happen to both of them. It is meaningful that they split up, singing together, this relationship which was promising in earlier days, but which is now at the edge of a precipice. This is the last demonstration of the couple´s union before they take, from now on, solitary directions which will take them to the fatal outcome: "Always lonely // And life goes on like this // I don't have who pities me // The end is coming to me." (51)

At the end of Act II, scene v, Lucíola sings Song 16 (72), As rosas não falam (Roses do not Speak) by Cartola, which is an Expression Song. This is a song that her grandmother used to sing every moment she missed her grandfather. Lucíola remembers that when her grandmother died she was singing that specific song, which becomes an expression of her soul, of her sorrowfulness, of her solitude, of her hopelessness and despair: the remembrance of this song is transformed into a foreboding of her death, which is a feeling that had also occurred earlier to her when she said: "My soul is cold with a feeling of death." (67)

Otelo recovers the status of a tragic hero in the musical after Dirceu´s real intentions are revealed by Marlene and Candinho. Otelo realizes that he had made part of a game of manipulation which had been put into action by Dirceu. Before he commits suicide, he sings Song 18 (85), Boêmio Fracassado (Failed Bohemian) by Hélio Cabral, which could be considered Otelo´s music, the music of his final moment when he expresses his wish to die while singing. In this song he discloses his heart, he recognizes his misfortune and mentions he will be smiling until the end even being sure that his happiness is only feigned. He finishes this song by asking the silvery moon to take his last kiss to his beloved Lucíola. This song, as many other ones of this theatre-musical, is an Expression Song.

When Otelo´s music has finished, what remains is the muffled sound of the samba drum as in a funeral procession. The actors and actresses approximate and gather round the tragic scene. Tia Fé who had initiated the musical will also finish it together with the chorus (Song 19; 86). The closing scene of musical theatre, when portraying a tragedy, ends up in a positive atmosphere of reaffirmation of values: it is possible to observe that the initial atmosphere of exaltation of the opening music will prevail in the closing number of the musical. At the end, there is the predominance of a rising movement towards happiness: after driving away the happiness and Mangueira´s School losing its rhythm, the wind will take sadness away, the samba drum will beat even stronger and its green and pink flag will shine again because its force is tradition. The last stanza (86) reiterates the idea that "Mangueira´s flames will never extinguish, it will continue to be the first in samba, the first in poetry, the first in harmony and the first in emotion."

Gustavo Gasparani appropriated the narrative structure of Shakespeare´s *Othello* as a pretext to tell a different story. He created a touching green and yellow musical-theatre when he transposed the Venetian Moor into the Brazilian cultural environment of popular music of the samba schools of Rio de Janeiro. He adapts the tragic sequence of events of the Shakespearian plot to suit his own purposes: the population of the Mangueira is proud of their history and conquests which are narrated through the samba-lyrics that are perfectly integrated in the development of the dramatic action. The songs not only contribute to narrate the plot but also punctuate its most meaningful moments when the characters reveal their feelings, emotions, fears, frustrations, deceptions. The fact that at least half of the songs which enter into the composition of *Otelo da Mangueira* can be classified as *Songs of Expression* acquires a special significance in this context. Through the insertion of songs which are in a suitable relation not only with the development of the dramatic action but also with the expression of what goes on in the characters´ minds and souls, Gasparani succeeds in achieving an equivalence of function as concerns the Shakespearian soliloquies and asides which also express the characters' feelings and intimate thoughts.

Works Cited

Ewen. David. *The Story of America's Musical Theatre.* Philadelphia: Hilton, 1968.

Heliodora, B. *Falando de Shakespeare.* Sao Paulo: Perspectiva; Rio de Janeiro: Funarte: Cultura Inglesa, 1997. (Estudos; 155)

Gasparani, G. *Otelo da Mangueira.* Roteiro de Encenacao. (3° tratamento—Marco de 2005).

Kenrick, John. *How Musicals are Made; How to Write a Musical.* Copyright 2000-2004; Text Revised 2009. http://www.musicals 101.com/write.htm

_____. *Elements of a Musical; The Score.* Copyright 2000; Text Revised 2003. <http://www.musicals101.com/score.htm>;

Kott, Ian. *Shakespeare our Contemporary.* London: Routledge, 1994.

Pavis, Patrice. *Dicionário de teatro* (Trad.) J. Guinsburg e Ma. Lúcia Pereira. São Paulo: Perspectiva, 1999.

Segato, Rita L. *Santos e Daimones:* o politeísmo afro-brasileiro e a tradicao arquetipal. 2. ed. Brasília: Editora Universidade de Brasília, 2005.

Shakespeare, W. *Othello, the Moor of Venice, The Complete Works of William Shakespeare.* New York: Gramercy Books, 1990. (1113-1150).

Text, Performance and Film: An Intermedial Reading of Antunes Filho´s *Throne of Blood/Macbeth*

LIANA DE CAMARGO LEAO
MAIL MARQUES DE AZEVEDO
UFPR, Curitiba, Pr, Brasil
UNIANDRADE, Curitiba, Pr, Brasil

> "Shakespeare´s plays, with their inherently flexible structure and openness of style, positively invite distinctive re-interpretation on performance." John Russell Brown

Throne of Blood/Macbeth, the title of Brazilian director Antunes Filho´s staging of the Shakespearean tragedy, refers explicitly to Akira Kurosawa´s film, and puts into relief its intermedial characteristics. In fact, the director carried his well-known devotion to the cinema into the organization of the CPT, Centro de Pesquisa Teatral (Theatrical Research Center), where the play was produced, in 1993. Antunes has imbued the CPT with the spirit of extensive research into the aesthetics of spectacle, which he deems indispensable for the formation of actors, playwrights, designers and personnel connected with stage performance in the courses provided by the Center. The use of film as a source has been common practice at the CPT.

Hence the objective of this paper to study the references in Antunes Filho's staging of *Macbeth* to Kurosawa´s film, primarily the use of filmic techniques having to do with details of setting—scenery, costumes, and masks—and performance, which stand in further intermedial relationship to the Japanese Noh theatre. A brief retrospect of Antunes Filho´s variegated career in the theatre antecedes the analysis of the elements mentioned above, and the discussion of how "the media product uses its own media-specific means to refer to a specific individual work produced in another medium" (Rajewsky, 44).

The metamorphosis of José Alves—artistic name of the would-be actor—into Antunes Filho, the *metteur-en-scène*, must have been received with joy by both theatrical audiences and critics, who were allowed to exchange a striving mediocre performer for today´s internationally acclaimed "poet of the scene." From the start involved in new artistic trends, the predominant attitude of Antunes Filho has been one of rebellion and freedom of creation.

Disrespect of laws and rules is nothing new in the life of Antunes Filho who as a boy had the run of the streets of a provincial São Paulo, involved in brawls in which purple eyes and broken bones were no obstacle to his undaunted courage. And who—as Sebastião Milaré tells us—loved the cinema almost as much as he loved soccer; was very fond of the circus, and led by his theatre-loving mother, developed a lifelong passion for everything having to do with dramatic texts and theatrical performance (Milaré, 2011).

A first job at City Hall, where he met Osmar Rodrigues Cruz, proved to be a springboard into the world of the theatre. The lukewarm reception of his performance as an actor in *Adeus, Mocidade*, directed by Cruz at the Conservatório Dramático Musical de Sao Paulo (Sao Paulo Conservatory of Drama and Music) gave him second thoughts about his acting ability, but did nothing to quench his enthusiasm for the theatre. He had found his artistic lifelong call.

At the time Sao Paulo was thriving with amateur theatrical enterprises, such as Alfredo Mesquita´s Experimental Group; the University Group, founded by Décio de Almeida Prado at the

University of Sao Paulo, and Paulo Autran´s Group of Amateur Artists. The creation of the TBC, Teatro Brasileiro de Comédia (Brazilian Theater of Comedy), in 1948, to house the three groups was a first step toward professionalization, furthered by the hiring of Italian directors Luciano Salce, Adolfo Celi, Flamínio Bollini Cerri, Ruggero Jacobbi—besides the renowned Polish director Zigbiniew Ziembinski. In one way or another, the young José Alves was closely associated with all these movements and tendencies.

Still set on an acting career, his final unsuccessful attempt in 1950—he was rejected in the selection test for the cast of *Our Town*, to be directed by his friend Osmar Cruz, (a matter of much leg-pulling later on in the theatrical milieu)—turned him definitely onto his path as director. The full measure of the energy and courage of his youth was then channeled to the achievement of his artistic objectives in staging.

His beginnings were modest with the founding of amateur groups which, nevertheless, called attention to his work, and landed him in the TBC as assistant-director to the Italian masters. From then on his curriculum has been marked mostly by loud successes (in spite of a few resounding failures), as a result of his determination "to attempt something of ambition and size" even if that meant being vulnerable to critical and even public rejection.

His rendering of Shakespeare´s comedy *The Taming of the Shrew*, in 1965, makes a reflection over the accumulated knowledge of social life through the centuries—woman´s emancipation, man´s new role as money-maker rather than *pater familias*—and evidences his understanding of Shakespeare´s characters as prototypes of modern man. The introduction of the contemporary, such as bottles of Coke, a game of rugby and a chorus of Beattle songs, furthermore, made the play a huge success.

By contrast, the production of *Julius Caesar* was a stumbling block in the director´s ascending prestige. Inappropriate locale, lack of unity in the performance and other circumstances, such as a shocking naked Julius Caesar in a coffin on the stage, drew hoots and catcalls from both the galleries and the orchestra seats, notwithstanding the famous names in the cast.

Antunes Fillho´s ensuing attempts at commercial theatre, movie-making, and theatre on television were stepping stones leading to the creation of an actors´ course which originated the production of Mário de Andrade´s *Macunaíma* and, as a corollary, the institution of the CPT. The craftsman had gone back to the basic material of his art—the human soul—but carrying in his luggage valuable ideas and experiences collected along his journey.

Antunes Filho´s choice of title for his play, *Throne of Blood/ Macbeth*, is both an explicit reference to Akira Kurosawa´s film and an illustration of his devotion to the cinema: "Oh, the two things, theatre and cinema. The dramatic expression always had me. The human adventure always touched me deeply." "Dramatic expression" on the stage necessarily differs from dramatic expression on the screen and the analysis of an intermedial relationship between the two, established by artists who enjoy free transit in both media is challenging, to say the least.

Following primarily Irina Rajewsky's approach to intermediality as a category for the concrete analysis of texts or other kinds of media products, this paper is structured along rather conventional lines: basically the analysis of theme, scenic space, rhythm of the action, and actors' performance, against the backdrop of dialogue between the arts, namely Antunes Filho´s play (1993) and Kurosawa´s film (1957), hereon referred to as *Throne of Blood* and *The Castle of the Spider´s Web*, respectively.

The term "re-mediation," as used by the critic, aptly describes the intermedial relationship between Kurosawa´s and Antunes´s versions of *Macbeth*, as well as their references to other arts. Although separated by nearly half a century, the theatrical and the cinematic readings of the tragedy have uncannily similar characteristics.

Brazilian scholar Sebastião Milaré´s extensive studies of Antunes Filho´s artistic activities evidence two aspects of special relevance for this analysis: his developed sense of Japanese culture and the reliance on literary sources for his plays.

Those are in fact recreation rather than straightforward adaptation of their sources. Antunes Filho´s appropriation of *Macbeth*, for instance, is not a mere transposition of Shakespeare´s text but its performance mediated by Japanese culture and, more specifically, by Akira Kurosawa´s film *The Castle of the Spider´s Web*, which in its turn is a re-writing of Shakespeare´s *Macbeth*.

The Japanese influence on the conception of *Throne of Blood/ Macbeth*—homage to Kurosawa´s genius—simultaneously gives the play a sense of exoticism and of the universal, as the Brazilian production is neither a copy of the Japanese film nor a pseudo-British *montage*: it is a reworking of influences and traditions.

It is not the aim of this paper to explore the obvious parallels between *The Castle of the Spider´s Web* and the Noh theatre, which has been the object of hundreds of skilled commentators. Only a few aspects of Kurosawa´s adaptation are dealt with here in counterpoint with Antunes´s reading.

While Kurosawa eschews verbal language in favor of images and the action proper—visual images, action, gestures and Noh rituals are substituted for most of Shakespeare´s famous soliloquies and dialogues—Shakespeare´s text holds a prominent place in the Brazilian production. The bard´s authorship is highlighted in the programme of the production, where no references are made to the translator of the play. The whole project repeatedly refers to Shakespeare as the author and establishes Antunes as responsible for the adaptation. Moreover, it is undeniable that the play retells the familiar story of *Macbeth* and its characters, both recognizable by the spectator, in spite of the radical abridging of the text—the production ran for a little over an hour and forty minutes. Antunes possibly made use of several Brazilian translations in order to construct his adapted text, which is rendered in prose.

Recognizing Kurosawa´s film as an adaptation of Shakespeare´s *Macbeth*, unless explicitly announced in the credits, however, requires knowledge of the play´s *fabula*, since the characters are given different names, in accordance with the Japanese historical background and cultural tradition. Early in the development of the filmic narrative, though, similar themes inspiring *Macbeth* come to the fore, basically the evil effects of the lust for power on even the bravest of characters, adapted to the specific situation of civil-war strife in medieval Japan.

The capacity of the Shakespearean text to be made to fit diverse periods of the history of mankind tells of its inherent political vocation.

***Macbeth*´s Political Vocation**

Macbeth is Shakespeare´s sole Scottish play, and its first performance occurred at Hampton Court, for the benefit of England´s equally single Scottish king, James I, the patron of the troupe of actors, The King´s Men. Contemporary events are reflected in the play: the witch trials of 1590-91 conducted by James, who wrote a treatise on *Daemonologie* (1597); the Gunpowder plot; the genealogy of the kings who descended from Banquo, who was changed from the role of Macbeth´s accomplice in the murder of Duncan into that of his enemy, obviously with the intention of pleasing James IV.

Throughout the centuries, the political vocation of the play has been asserting itself in the production of numerous adaptations that fit the context of different countries and states. The background of Orson Welles´s 1936 stage production, for instance, is the revolution in the Caribbean; in Welles´s 1948 version, though, it is no longer Haiti but fascism that provides the political key to the film. Roman Polanski´s 1970 version has been linked to the violence of the Second World War and of the Cold War. Kurosawa transfers the action to a medieval Japan wrought by civil wars in the sixteenth century.

For Antunes Filho, the production of *Macbeth* threw light on the Brazilian political reality of the 90s, when the people´s hope for democracy and the desire of the intelligentsia for freedom of expression were rudely shattered by the corruption of Fernando Collor de Mello´s government, the first president to be directly elected by the people, after twenty years of military rule. Collor was forced to resign office in August 1992, formally accused of "High Crimes and Misdemeanors." This does not make the production topical, although spectators with an eye on the news can easily draw parallels between the play and the Brazilian political scenario: if a people can emerge from a somber period of dictatorship, by electing its President, it might as well put on a play that condemns a tyrant.

Good and Evil

"Ambiguous oracles which, by their literal fulfillment, deceive them who confide in them" trigger Macbeth´s entanglement "in the snares of hell." Coleridge´s critical commentaries, however, eschew the inexorability of destiny as the propelling principle of Shakespeare´s tragedy. In his view, "the poet wishes to show that the conflict of good and evil in this world can only take place by the permission of Providence, which converts the curse that individual mortals draw down on their heads into a blessing to others" (in Staunton, 2049).

Whatever interpretation may be ascribed to the transformation of Macbeth from fearless warrior into ruthless assassin, it is his fierce inner struggle between good and evil that furnishes the guidelines of the hero´s characterization and commands the dénouement of his tragedy. In spite of his torment, nevertheless, it is clear that ambition prevails and Macbeth´s decision to kill Duncan is an act of free will.

Antunes Filho´s staging enhances Macbeth´s compulsive descent into a world of shadows and darkness from the moment he lends ears to the witches´ prophecies to his death at the hands of Macduff. As in Shakespeare´s original text, Macbeth wages a losing battle against his own inner darkness, made up of remorse at having murdered his king, and of his cruel resolve to betray, deceive and kill whoever may thwart his lust for power.

The reflection on good and evil is not an isolated topic in Antunes´s theatrical productions. In his book *Hierofania: o teatro segundo Antunes Filho* (2010), Sebastião Milaré includes an analysis of *Throne of Blood* in the chapter called "Sinergia do mal" ("Evil Synergy"), in which he groups the play with two other of the director´s productions—*Velha nova estória and Vereda da Salvação*—both centering on the exploration of evil. Milaré sees this phase as having continuity with the coming production of *Gilgamesh and Drácula e outros vampiros*, both of which explore the poetics of immortality and the myth of the tree of life. Together the five plays are a meditation about the human condition as envisaged at the end of the twentieth century.

Antunes´s familiarity with Oriental philosophies that conceptualize good and evil as complementary—good does not exist without evil and evil does not exist without good—adds a further link with Kurosawa´s reading of the Shakespearean text. It is man´s task to learn how to deal both with good and evil. Coherently, Antunes aims at "discussing man in his limits" in his staging of Macbeth. "The great evil, great goodness" and especially to be aware of seduction, "to fear seduction; every seduction is dangerous, especially political seduction" (Antunes, 1996). "Discussing man at his limits" is the director´s primary concern and the reason for his valorization of the actor´s function as the axis of the theatrical performance.

Masks

Kurosawa was not interested in reproducing Shakespeare´s verbal language not even to help his actors compose their characters. He chose instead to use Noh masks as models, in order to impress on his actors how to express controversial feelings of fear and anger, elation and despair, that threaten to tear apart bodies and souls.

For the composition of Lord Washizu, Toshiro Mifune, Kurosawa´s favorite actor, was shown the mask of Heida, the warrior; the actress playing the Lady Asaji, was introduced to the mask of Shakumi, a beautiful woman, no longer young, who is on the brink of madness; to compose the Evil Spirit, the Yamanba mask; to compose Mik, the mask of Chûjô, the nobleman (in Cardullo, 65; 103) The scheme below helps the visualization of Kurosawa´s strategy:

Traditional Nōh Theater masks and their THRONE OF BLOOD counterparts

Toshiro Mifune´s dark beard and savage features add the warmth of the flesh and blood actor to his strikingly faithful reproduction of the Noh mask, in his impersonation of the fierce warrior, Lord Washizu. The complete symbiosis Isuzu Yamada-Sakaji-Lady Asaji further evidences the Japanese director´s ability. Yamada´s Lady Asaji (Lady Macbeth) is terrifyingly unemotional, in contrast to the intensity of Mifune´s performance, and enhances the dramatic impact of her influence over her husband.

Antunes will refer to the Noh masks in his protagonists´ make-up: Luiz Melo´s heavily marked dark eyebrows and moustache, his long hair topped by the helmet or the crown, are similar to the features of his counterpart, a samurai in feudal Japan; Samantha Monteiro´s composition of Lady Macbeth, whitish complexion in sharp contrast with thick black eyebrows, comes even closer to Kurosawa´s conception of the Shakespearean character.

In her commentaries about Antunes´s production, Lilian Lopondo takes special notice of the Noh influence on Samantha Monteiro´s performance: "Walking in Noh fashion, without gestures, the facial immobility of Lady Macbeth masks the determination of her spirit, noticeable through the power and impact of her voice, which seems to spew forth from her entrails."

Actually, the characterization of Lady Macbeth in *Throne of Blood* is exemplary of its director´s methods centered mostly on his work with the actor, from whom absolute consciousness of space is demanded; not merely of the physical concrete *mise-en-scène*, but of the play as a whole, both its external, visible aspect of dramatic progression, and its deeper meaning. The actor is required to develop a feeling of the character through his own body and emotions. In Sebastião Milare´s view the actor is the vehicle for Antunes´s research into the nature of the theater. As for the physical space of the performance, the stage is the actor´s domain and it is his perception of space that determines the geometry of his own movements.

Thus, the key function of concrete details of stage setting, lighting and costumes is to lend support to the work of the actor, who makes use of the concrete in order to achieve transcendence.

Intermedial references in *Throne of Blood* to Kurosawa´s film in this study, as stated above, have to do primarily with details of setting—scenery, costumes, and masks—and their consequent influence on the actors´ performance. Costumes are especially prominent as one of the play´s "constitutional strategies that contribute to the media product's overall signification" in the case when "the media product uses its own media-specific means . . . to refer to a specific, individual work produced in another medium" (Rajewsky, 2006, 52).

Costumes

Designed by artist Romero Lima, costumes are made of patches cut off velvet draperies; the use of samurai swords and headgear confirm the Japanese imprint of the production. As "constitutional strategies," costumes and character attitudes have special signification in *Throne of Blood*. The messenger dressed in rags, who brings bad news, barely escapes being choked to death in the explosion of Macbeth´s wrath, in spite of subserviently kneeling in front of his king. The similarly cringing attitude of a foot soldier, fully attired in the samurai fashion down to the arrows protruding from the back of his armor,—far from surprising in the Japanese setting—has specific resonance in the recreation of Shakespeare´s Scottish ambience of the play, where there is no room for servility. Actors and, consequently, spectators are led to search for the deeper meaning of such discrepancies, actually the main objective of Antunes Filho´s *mise-en-scène* as well as of his entire conception of *Throne of Blood.*

Lima´s work is described by the historian and costume designer Luciana Buarque as being "neither clothes nor props; they are complete figures, live sculptures that seem to have escaped from ancient fable books, religious patterns, tarot cards." Buarque suggests further that characters as conceived by Rogerio Lima "are not types, but archetypes, Macbeth is not a king, but all kings, with the weight and the seduction that power brings; Lady Macbeth is not merely an evil Queen, she is the serpent of Paradise, the Medusa" (Buarque, 1993, 25). Samantha Monteiro´s composition of Lady Macbeth as a serpent that tempts the hero is made into a visual icon of the serpent´s perfidy by means of her long braided hair, in itself an intermedial reference to Japanese culture and Kurosawa´s film.

The striking similarity between the images of the theatrical and the filmic rendering of Lady Macbeth provides further evidence on the intermedial relationship between Antunes Filho´s play and Kurosawa´s film.

Scenic Space

Scenic space in *Throne of Blood* was conceived by one of the most influential scenographers in Brazil, J.C. Serroni, who declared that his basic idea was a "free stage for the actors" and "a scenographic framework," a space limited by heavy walls which have the function of suggesting an atmosphere of oppression and imprisonment,—human beings trapped like animals in a cage and as such deprived of rationality—rather than faithfully reproducing any particular place, Serroni aimed at a multiple and ambiguous space, one which would invite the public to imagine various universes.

And this is precisely the achievement of his scenic design which alludes to the shape of a medieval Japanese Castle, as depicted in Kurosawa´s film: huge heavy doors and gates, giving access to or surrounding large quadrangular-shaped empty spaces. The two figures below illustrate the striking similarity between Serroni´s scenery and Kurosawa´s castle.

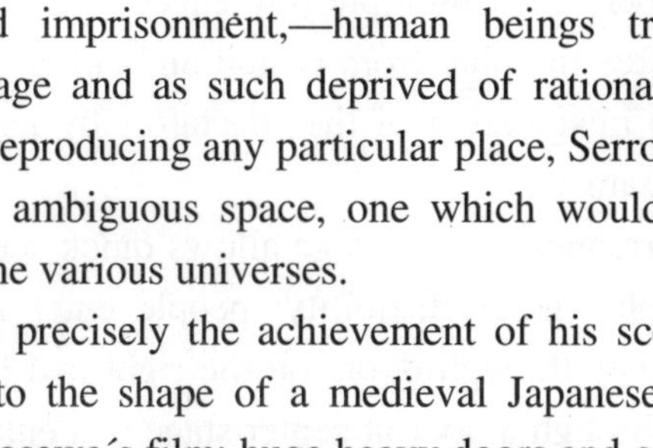

Besides the intermedial reference to Kurosawa´s film and, consequently, to the bare scenery of the Noh theater, Serroni pays tribute to the theater in Shakespeare´s time by referring to the architecture of both the inn-yard and of the Elizabethan theater proper. Such multiple references to other stages, spaces and times free the play from period and cultural specificity and liberate the imagination of the spectators by lending the action universal character.

The barrenness of the stage allows quick scene changes and gives the play great flexibility: people enter and exit almost simultaneously through doors on the right and left of the stage, as well as through a door at center stage. An enlarged version of the Elizabethan balcony provides two other ways in and out of the stage through a door on each side. Four large windows facing the audience, in the center of the balcony, provide frames for the intervention of frightening supernatural apparitions that remind Macbeth of his sins. A ladder on the right gives access to the second floor. At two different crucial points in the action, the actor playing Macbeth descends to the ground using a rope that hangs from the roof.

After Duncan´s murder the naked stage with its barren gray walls is used as an invisible prison or, to refer specifically to Kurosawa´s image, as an impenetrable maze: Lady Macbeth, and particularly Macbeth, haunted by their fearful thoughts run from wall to wall in nightmarish movements.

The red painted stage floor is the only striking color in the whole scenario, contrasting sharply with the grayish walls. The red color makes reference to the title of the performance as well as to the motif of blood—the battles that open and close the play and the violent assassination of King Duncan—followed by the merciless killing of whoever stood in Macbeth´s path to the throne.

Lighting

It is undeniable that *The Castle of the Spider´s Web* possesses a painterly quality. It is common knowledge that as a youth Kurosawa aspired to be a painter, and later on, as a film director, he made use of the techniques of painting, balancing each frame as a pictorial composition and displaying great understanding of contrast. The film designer, Yoshiro Muraki, reveals that mist and fog were used to contrast with black armored walls and also with the black volcanic soil as shown in the film, all contributing to a *suiboku-ga* or *sumi-e* effect. (cited Richie, 1991) In his appraisal of the film, Richard Prince also connects its aesthetics to the *sumi-e*: large portions of the picture are left unfilled, emptiness being a positive compositional value in the *sumi-e*; "striking emptiness of the spaces—the skies, the dense fog that obscures mountains and plains—is a cinematic rendition of *sumi-e* composition. As a positive value, this pictorial and spiritual "emptiness" is set against the human world of vanity, ambition, and violence, which Kurosawa suggests is all illusion" (Prince, 2003).

Antunes follows Kurosawa in the creation of the contrast of dark and light. Through scenography, costumes, make-up and lighting, the Brazilian production imprints a sense of black-and-white to the spectacle, with the exception of the red floor.

Color is introduced in those scenes related to supernatural beings as, for instance, the green lighting and the candles at the scene of the banquet. In the second witches' scene, the three eerie beings are surrounded by diffuse blue lighting, whereas a strong greenish light is projected on ghost-like apparitions at the upper-stage windows.

The conception of the three phantasmagorical sisters is borrowed from Greek mythology: they are the three Moirai, or the three Fates—the Parcae in Roman mythology—Clotho, Lachesis and Atropos, depicted as ugly old women dressed in long white robes, who command the destiny of every human being. Man´s fate is symbolized by the thread they weave which is Atropos´ task to cut, when man´s life reaches its close.

Antunes has the witches descend from the skies in a *mechane* to announce Macbeth´s fate. Two male actors impersonate the sisters, the third one being a dumb doll, hardly distinguishable from the living actors at first sight. The dumb doll may have functioned either as a device to save an actor from doubling up, or as a reference to the role of the third sister: cutting the thread of life. By choosing male actors, and for that matter, bearded ones, to impersonate the sisters, Antunes was bowing to the Elizabethan stage practice where male actors perform feminine roles and, also and moreover, conforming to Banquo´s description of the characters as "So wither'd and so wild in their attire, // That look not like the inhabitants of the earth, // And yet are on't? Live you? or are you aught // That man may question? You seem to understand me, // By each at once her chappy finger laying // Upon her skinny lips: you should be women, // And yet your beards forbid me to interpret // That you are so" (1.3. 39-47).

The three sisters of Greek mythology are condensed by Kurosawa into the sole image of an old hag incessantly turning the spinning wheel that weaves the destiny of Lord Washizu, as the future master of the "Castle of the Spider´s Web." The ambiguous male/female character of the evil spirit of the forest which follows Banquo´s description is represented in the film through the mostly male tones of its computerized voice.

Intermediality and Performance

Robert Stam points out that whereas "the matter of expression of literature is words, and only words, cinema is a composite language by virtue of its diverse matters of expression and thus 'inherits' all the art forms associated with these matters of expression" (2000, 35). In fact, filmic narrative can virtually absorb any kind of pre-existing discourse or expression. The richness of Kurosawa´s highly valued art lies precisely in the exploration of cinema as a multi-track medium. Thus he transposes Shakespeare´s text to the screen not as translation but as a profound transformation of the source into the savage world of medieval Japan. The alternation between battle scenes, that the medium allows, and the intimate moments that are the province of great theatrical performances forms a coherent whole that the Brazilian director equally achieves by means of the specific resources of his theatrical montage.

The analysis of Shakespeare´s text, in counterpoint to Antunes Filho´s staging and Kurosawa´s film, in the dénouement of the tragedy, brings out the characteristic traits of each medium.

In the last scene of Shakespeare´s text, Macduff presents Macbeth´s severed head to Malcolm and his victorious army:

> Hail, King, for so thou art. Behold where stands
> The usurper´s cursed head. The time is free
> I see thee compassed with thy kingdom´s pearl,
> That speak my salutation in their minds;
> Whose voices I desire aloud with mine
> Hail King of Scotland! (Act V 9.20-25)

The printed word, "the matter of expression of literature" is a flexible abstract medium which opens the way to signification. Thus, the word "pearl" can be a metaphor for the nobility of Scotland, or a metonymic term for "crown." Anyway, the poet chooses words that indicate the restoration of the political order.

Kurosawa´s film, on the contrary, does not bring any definite solution to the reigning political instability. An unending cycle of violence will inevitably result from Washizu´s assassination in his castle by his own men, an act which subverts the hierarchical social order. With the obliteration of distinctions that define culture, by the crossing over of boundaries between the master and his vassals, a web of mistrust, treason and violence is substituted for the harmonious living of the social group. Thus the throne, as the symbol of power, is irrevocably stained in blood. The figure below that shows Toshiro Mifune and "about one hundred arrows" is most impressive when visualized in film, to the accompaniment of the sibilant rain of arrows. It takes the resources of the medium: movement, synchronized sound, close-ups and/or panoramic shots to construct the image of the defeated fearful warrior effectively.

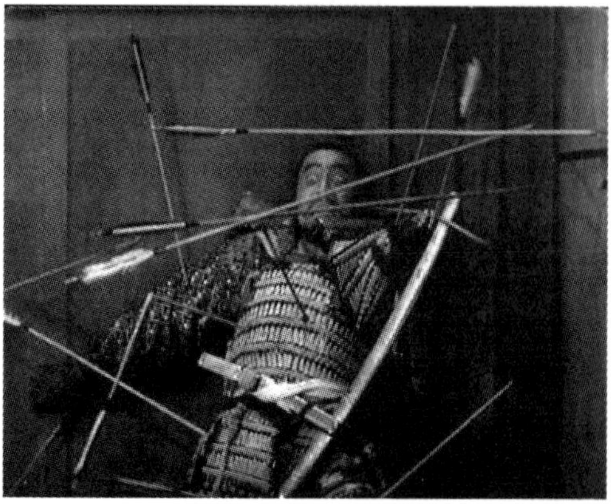

In Antunes's staging Luís Melo is shown in the cruel spastic movements of the agony that precedes death. The protagonist´s body is dragged on the stage by a rope, like a sacrificial victim. The raucous sound of the heavy-metal band, Kreator, accompanies the makeshift ritual. Evil is still rampant like an indelible stain of blood on the state itself, and, as indicated by the title of the montage, on the throne now permanently stained in blood.

Acknowledgements

This essay is the result of the approximation between university professors and theater practice. We departed from a careful viewing of the video of Antunes Filho´s *Throne of Blood/ Macbeth* (Brazilian Archive, MIT) and from the analysis of program notes and critical reviews of the play´s performance, kindly supplied by Rodrigo Audi from the CTP, to whom we owe deep thanks.

We owe a particular debt of gratitude to Sebastião Milaré for generously making available to us part of his still to be published research on Antunes Filho, as well as for sharing valuable ideas and commentaries on the performance of *Throne of Blood.*

Many thanks go to our indefatigable friends, Professor Marlene Soares dos Santos, for reading parts of this text, and Professor Anna Stegh Camati, always prompt with advice and encouragement.

Works Cited

Antunes Filho. Entrevista do encenador (Interview with Director) ao Diario de Sao Paulo, 04 de dezembro de 1973 (Dec. 4, 1973).

_____, Entrevista (Interview). *Jornal Estado de Sao Paulo*, 14 de agosto de 1996 (August 14, 1996).

Brown, John Russell. "*Shakespeare, Theatre and Cultural Politics*" *Shakespeare Survey,* n. 48, 1995.

Cardullo, Bert, ed. *Akira Kurosawa: Interviews.* University Press of Mississippi, 2008.

Manvell, Roger. *Shakespeare and the Film.* New York, 1971.

Milaré, Sebastiao. *Antunes Filho e a dimensão utópica.* São Paulo: Perspectiva, 1994.

___________ "*Convergencia Brasil-Japao no Teatro.*" *Revista USP* n. 27, sept./nov. 1995.

___________ *Hierofania: o teatro segundo Antunes Filho.* Sao Paulo: Edições SESC Sao Paulo, 2010.

___________ "Primeiros tempos" *Poeta da Cena* (2011).

Rajewsky, Irina. "Intermediality, Intertextuality and Remediation: A Literary Perspective on Intermediality." *Intermédialités*, n. 6, p. 43-61, Autumn 2006.

W. Shakespeare, *Macbeth*, ed. Kenneth Muir, Arden Shakespeare; 2nd ed. 1997.

Stam, Robert & Miller, Toby, ed. *Film and Theory. An Anthology.* Maiden Ms: Blackwell, 2000.

Staunton, Howard, ed. *The Globe Illustrated Shakespeare. The Complete Works. Annotated.* New York: Gramercy Books, 1972.

[In]fidelity in Translation: Shakespeare in Argentina

MIGUEL A. MONTEZANTI

The purpose of this article is to illustrate the reception of some Shakespearean plays in Argentina. Part 1 focuses on the limitations imposed by the audience's moral taste upon the translator's choices. Part 2 analyzes two cases in which SL texts have been heavily transformed, i.e. "appropriated" by two Argentine contemporary playwrights.

Translation

Eric Partridge reflects upon the hypothetical reception of his work: he conjectures, for instance, that it could have been published in the eighteenth century, but not in the Victorian period (xi). This is the general orientation I have in mind to see the problem in terms of translation. My first step will consist in comparing the translations of some strong words through the consideration of four versions of *Othello* currently available in Argentina. The first one does not mention the translator's name. The second is a translation by Jaime Clark. The third one was done by Rolando Costa Picazo, and the fourth, by Jaime Collyer. I shall refer to them as follows: UT (unknown translator), JC, CP and CO. Jaime Clark published a five-volume edition of ten plays by Shakespeare in Spain between 1872 and 1876. It is significant that a roughly 120 year-old translation is now republished in Barcelona, a powerful centre of the publishing industry. The third one forms part of a series in which the didactic purposes are evident.

Concerning the fourth translation (CO), its general orientation is "to give rigorous but up-to-date versions by those who are dealing with poetic matters equivalent to the ones that Shakespeare resolved four centuries ago."[1] The author states that these versions should avoid the "reverential awe" towards the bard and that they have been done by Latin American writers.

UT and CO are prose translations. JC chooses the current 11-syllable Spanish line to match the English verse sections, and translates the prose passages in prose, thus keeping the general contrast between the loftier speeches of the "public" characters and the more vulgar ways of Iago. CP does not try to recreate rhythm or rhymes except for some couplets which normally close a scene.

I shall follow the definition of euphemism given by K. Allan and K. Burridge: "A euphemism is used as an alternative to a dispreferred expression in order to avoid possible loss of face, either one's own face or, through giving offence, that of the audience, or of some third party."

The cases which I propose in ST show no avoidance of the strong terms used to insult a woman.[2] I will consider eight occurrences of "whore": The results are the following (figures indicate the number of occurrences):

UT: "*ramera*"= 2, "adulterous"= 2, "infidel"= 1, "paramour"= 1, "cunning girl"= 1, "Venetcian"= 1.
JC: "*ramera*"= 1, "prostitute"= 2, "adulterous"= 2, "cunning girl"= 1, "cunning courtesan"= 1, "mistress"= 1.
CP: "*puta*" = 4, "*ramera*"= 4.
CO: "*ramera*"= 7, "little whore"= 1.

CP is bold enough to use the strongest Spanish word to render "whore." All the translators mitigate Desdemona's boldness in (6), when she utters "I cannot say 'whore'."[3] As a rule, choices are weaker than the insistent word used by Shakespeare.[4]

Next I will consider eight occurrences of the word "strumpet": These are the results:

> UT: "*ramera*" = 3, "meretricious"= 1, "adulterous"= 1, "infamous = 1 (2 ST occurrences are not translated).
> JC: "prostitute"= 4, "ramera"= 3, "perfidious s= 1.CP: "*ramera*"= 5, "prostitute"= 2 (1 ST occurrence is not translated).
> CO: "*ramera*"= 4, "*ramerilla*"= 1, "*putilla*"= 2 (1 ST occurrence is not translated).

The strongest word, "[*P*]*uta*" is never used. By far "*ramera*" is definitely the preferred word. It is noticeable that UT and JC use the adjectives "*infamous*" and "*perfidious*," omitting the nouns. However, these adjectives do not necessarily refer to sexual matters. It can be seen that four occurrences of ST "strumpet" are not translated at all: omission or substituting only an adjective are ways of softening the impact of "dirty" words upon the readership. I link CP's choices with new "democratic" practices in Argentina, i.e. some slackening of formality or rigidness to be associated with the last dictatorship, not necessarily shared by CO, which forms part of a series addressed to a whole Latin American audience. I find a dynamic, *increscendo* strategy in the occurrences of the strong word for "whore" chosen by CP. There is a reluctance to use this strong term in the other translations, as if wishing to weaken Othello's coarseness.

It is understandable that JC avoided the strong term: not only because of linguistic and moral tastes, but also because this is a verse translation, normally associated with "poetic" prestige and manners. Similar prudish considerations apply to UT, which is apparently more recent than JC: it must be understood that the publishers of a cheap book which belongs to a series called "*Biblioteca de formación literaria*" [Library for Literary Upbringing] must have had in mind secondary school students.[5]

The procedures for this are manifold, i.e. omission, derivation through suffixes, hyperonyms.

Appropriation

My examples of appropriation are two: *Macbeth* and *Hamlet.* The first, by Griselda Gambaro, is given the title *La señora Macbeth.* Griselda Gambaro is one of the best known contemporary playwrights in Argentina. About the foreign influences that she might have received, she considers that tracing back connections with European writers implies accepting a colonialist spirit which has been imposed from the centres. She identifies with marginalized people and "innocent trespassers." She knows that her plays have been compared with Michel Foucault's theory of power, but she says she prefers poetry or fiction to essays.

La señora Macbeth was staged in 2004 in Buenos Aires. The characters are few: Lady Macbeth, the three Witches and the Ghost of Banquo. On stage there is a huge throne attached to a grotesque swing and a toboggan. The witches are not fully presented as such: they appear as maids or as a chorus. The language is Riverplate dialect but it contains some strange features. For example, the formal addressing form, "*señora*" [lady] demands a corresponding pronominal formality, i.e. "*Ud.*" and the verbal forms that go with it. Instead, all the verbal forms correspond to the informal and local pronoun "*vos*": this creates an odd atmosphere, a mixture of respect and confidence reinforcing the fact that the witches sneer at *la señora* while obeying her. Without any trace of rudeness, the style resorts to several colloquial expressions, some of them originated in football popular jargon.

La señora Macbeth comprehends six scenes. Lady Macbeth appears as a compassionate, slightly ridiculous woman: she wants to welcome the King offering a banquet for poor children. She declares that she wants to wash the children's feet, she is tender towards little animals as well. Her somehow silly discourse mixes impulses towards freedom and eroticism. It is coherent with the recognition that "I don't think anything. I leave thinking to Macbeth, who thinks for both of us." Her husband's letter, which she exhibits proudly, contains a syntactically strange though powerful formula: "*¡Salve rey, que serás!*" [Hail the King to be!]. Afterwards she blames the witches for having encouraged her husband to become a murderer. After the murder, in which she has been an accessory, she comforts Macbeth. Macbeth repents of his confession to his wife rather than of his desire to kill the king. Sc. 3 is a long monologue uttered by Lady Macbeth: eventually Macbeth had convinced his wife that inviting children would offend the king. The impressive passage about the dagger is reported in the following way: "It was Duncan who guided the dagger in Macbeth's hand and pointed it to his own heart to pierce it." News is manipulated, guilt vanishes: "Imprecise guilt is after an owner and when it does not find any it falls on anyone." The same manipulation happens when Banquo's Ghost appears. Lady Macbeth accuses him of being unthankful towards Macbeth, who wanted to give a banquet for him. At the end of this scene (sc. 4) we perceive that *la señora* hesitates: she does not know the extent of her responsibility in murders.

In the following scene the witches foretell that Macduff's wife and kids will be slaughtered. *La senora* refuses to believe them. Again, she blames the witches. But Macbeth, she says, would not dare to touch a child: "He is not a butcher, my Macbeth! Only a man with ambitions." Gambaro introduces theatre within the theatre: the witches personify Lady Macduff, her son and the murderer, while the Lady, astonished and chorus-like, contemplates what is going on. Lady Macduff says: "However, I remember that harm is sometimes praiseworthy in this world, and doing good is sometimes understood as a dangerous insanity. Then what is the use of this feminine defense in saying "I haven't harmed anybody"? Lady Macbeth refuses to believe that what she has witnessed is just a masquerade. Then the witches command her to look at her hands: they are tainted with blood. In the following monologue *la señora* breaks a mirror (a combination of *Snow White* and *Richard II*): at this moment she discovers that she is many *señoras* Macbeth, one of them rejecting the other. Theatrical representation and reality become confused. A report is given on how the prophecy about the wood of Birnam and Macbeth's defeat are being fulfilled. *La señora* Macbeth dies.

Gambaro said that she had not re-read Shakespeare's play in order to write her play. Pompeyo Audivert, who was in charge of the *mise en scène*, said that it was not necessary to have read *Macbeth* to understand Gambaro's play. Hints from Shakespeare are there: for example, when *la señora* says: "all the Arabian fragrances would not be enough to perfume this little hand"; when she realizes that Macbeth has killed sleep or when she mentions Macbeth's robes and crown as ill-fitting for him. It is more important to show how often *la señora* refers to children. Not only does *la señora* Macbeth think of inviting poor children, she also mentions her desire to give Macbeth sons who would replace Banquo's offspring on the throne. But when she becomes aware that the prophecy cannot be abolished, she does not care for them any longer. She discards frantically the idea of becoming Macbeth's daughter and eventually announces that she is going to procreate herself to become a queen (sc.1). Little birds, babies, *la señora* as an innocent baby, form part of an imagery that dwells on the idea of innocence and purity. However, the action can be deciphered in contemporary terms. For example, *la señora* speaks about the helplessness of a woman covered by a *chador* and humiliated, a revindication of Muslim women. More relevant is the speech in sc. 6, when she mentions corpses that appear in a ditch or in the river, a clear allusion to those who disappeared during the last Argentine dictatorship. In the same vein, several occurrences of the word "*poder*" give the idea of impersonal power: "And if corpses appear in a ditch or in the river, I am innocent of that action because my power has not commanded it." *La señora Macbeth* must be associated with brutal power but the suggestion is that, while loving Macbeth and admitting that she herself is ambitious, she does not share the decision to murder, she ignores the dead, she cannot believe that her husband is capable of such evils, and she eventually justifies crime on the ground of *raisons d'état*.

Gambaro has also emphasized the issue of the grotesque. In sc. 4, for example, the witches are trying to amuse *la señora* after the assassination of Duncan: they carry *la señora* to the top of the toboggan and push her down softly.[6] *La señora Macbeth* shows feminine subordination to, and acceptance of, male power. Olga Cosentino, writing in *Clarín*, an Argentine popular tabloid, says that *la señora* Macbeth can be connected with the wives of some contemporary tyrannical leaders: Imelda Marcos, Madame Mao, Nicolas Ceaucescu's wife and some other obvious local paradigms. The issue of identity can be illustrated at its best when one of the witches describes *la señora* as a transvestite. The emergence of different selves at the end of the play reveals paraphrenia. *La señora* asks: "Who am I? What is my nature? Am I perhaps a man wearing a woman's dress?"

The second case of appropriation is a play written by Luis Cano, *Hamlet, de William Shakespeare*. One can properly say that in it "time" (but also text) "is out of joint." Cano has said that *Hamlet* is a dream transformed into a nightmare. The sequence of events is looser than the one developed by Gambaro in *La señora Macbeth*. The atmosphere grows strange as we see dead characters resurrect. This happens with Polonius and Ophelia. The structure of the play can be described as if the "original" scenes had been heaped up, taken out and then recombined at random. Intertextuality is mainly achieved through allusion and paraphrase. Their scope is wide and can be shortly described as follows: passages from *Hamlet* are uttered by different characters, sometimes with changes. For example Polonius says: "If you are after the prince, here you are." Ophelia says, "What a piece of shit man is." Some passages are derived from the Sonnets: "No longer mourn for me," in English in Cano's play, is said by the Ghost. From *Richard III*: "My kingdom for a drink" is said by Rosencrantz and Guildenstern. Some passages are derived from a combination of *Macbeth* and *Hamlet*: the Digger says: "To dig implies an act and an act has three parts, to act, to do and to perform. That is the question!"; or from *The Tempest*: Fortinbras says: "We are made of the same stuff of our dead." There are allusions to other authors, for example Edgar Allan Poe ("The Raven," "The Fall of the House of Usher"); Jose Hernández (*Martín Fierro*, the Argentine national poem); c) T.S. Eliot (*The Love Song of J. Alfred Prufrock*); d) Lord Byron (directly mentioned); e) the Gospels, when the King says: "You'll find a sheep tied. Unfasten it and bring it here. And if somebody asks you about it, you'll answer 'My father needs it'"; the Parable of the Solid Rock, the *Genesis*, etc.

Thus, the general plot functions as a sort of skeleton which sustains three sequences. One of these is theatrical practices. Contemporary theatrical Argentine discourses are criticized. Illusion is broken in a Brechtian way when the King says "I am the best Danish actor"; Horatio mentions a contemporary local author together with Richard Burton. Hamlet says "This four hundred year-old play that I wrote just a month ago." An actor comments ironically that the speeches cannot be learned by heart if they are continually changed. Comments are made by Hamlet about a humiliated actor's ambition to utter "To be or not to be" soliloquy. Finally, there is Horatio's invitation to settle the limits between reality and fiction as *Verfremdungseffekt*: "Let us play a game. Let us pretend that all of us are dead and kings with motionless eyes. Snow kings in the sun. You, who look pale and dumb actors." In the same vein, the King's speech, if slightly mocking, comments upon theatrical practices. He praises the play, announces that TV broadcasting is on schedule, declares that art can achieve salvation, that the play has got its copyright, and that actors have new opportunities for work. The King's superiority reflects obliquely King Claudius's speeches, but his opinions entail a metacomment on performances, on the play, on Argentine contemporary situation, on modern theatrical practices.

The second focus is the author's complex relationship with Shakespeare, perhaps *via* Stephen Dedalus. Cano spoke about his obsession with Hamlet and with authorship: "As I reread Shakespeare's play it seems to me that I am deciphering the history of a life that was once mine." Shakespeare is the ghost who writes Cano, a familiar ghost, a spectator of Cano's writing. Cano feels he is sometimes Hamlet, or Ophelia, or madness, or Burbage performing Hamlet. A sort of chorus says: "Shakespeare? I know of his name. He is the one who writes like Byron. I don't believe you know Byron. No, this is not Shakespeare's *Hamlet*. *Hamlet* was finished when Shakespeare wrote the last word. Boring, rancid, insipid." In Act 2 Horatio exclaims: "Hamlet, living with him / how boring! / he is always grunting and crying / . . . his magnificent speeches." Luis Cano is facing the same problem Pierre Menard faces: authorship being put at stake through anachronism and wrong attributions. This seems to me Luis Cano's most interesting accomplishment in the play, showing that *Hamlet* (or any significant work) must be reinvented from time to time. This blurs the boundaries between translation and adaptation.[7]

Moreover, as Carlos Pacheco notices, Cano's play shows no perceptible differences in the language the characters use, as if any of them could, so to say, take up Hamlet's voice. This happens as if an anonymous power were governing them all, "washing at their identities," in Philip Larkin's phrase. A mixture of languages highlights the problem of authorship. In 1.11 the Ghost speaks in English but Hamlet does so in Spanish. Hamlet starts his soliloquy: "To be-no part of it" and goes on in Spanish. This mixture creates a pastiche effect which, reveals the permanent transformation of the author, who invents old fables, modifies them in a Protean way and uses several enigmatic vehicles.[8] Luis Cano's text is disruptive of theatrical practices in other ways: what can be read between brackets is not properly speaking stage directions: in many cases they are genuine speeches, i.e. "literary" or dramatic texts without any further direction. This involves a deliberate confusion of planes, i.e. the actors' speeches and the author's directions. The director has to decide whether off-voices (whose?) should utter these speeches or if actual actors (who?) are going to say them.

The third axis is the allusions to the Falklands-Malvinas war. The missing (as in Gambaro's play) and the victims of the Malvinas war are certainly two main obsessions in present Argentina. The first occurrence is a stage direction mentioning iron scoria and dismantled buildings.[9] When the play was staged, the Danish palace had the appearance of military headquarters in the open air, rust and saltpetre corroding everything. Horatio mentions cannons and parachutists in fancy dress. Hamlet says he has just come from a shooting practice in which he had to stab some cardboard English men.

The Malvinas setting justifies many occurrences of the word "sheep," significantly in the above-mentioned passage from the Gospels, where "sheep" replaces the donkey fetched by the Apostles. Allusion becomes straightforward when Goosegreen, a place in the Malvinas is mentioned. The monologue in which Hamlet is shocked by Fortinbras' warlike march to repossess a territory is paraphrased in sc. 3. Hamlet mentions seven hundred soldiers (roughly the sum of Argentine casualties) fighting for a piece of land not large enough to bury them.[10] The most straightforward allusions occur in 4.11: Hamlet reports that he has been murdering Englishmen. Then he has fastened the sheep his father was going to torture. Horatio mentions the ship that would not sink (the *General Belgrano* Cruiser (an Argentine ship that was sunk in the War), *The Invincible* (a British boat, which was seriously damaged), *The Titanic*?). Both Hamlet and Horatio recollect how they have come; brought by the last aircraft, all their dead friends sheltered under a little blanket. "The Boss arrived to visit us, always drunk. He came with his parachute." At this moment the King asks: "Where are we going to place the army club, the dining room, the bathrooms?" Algae ("kelpers," i.e. the inhabitants of the Islands) and sheep are insistently mentioned. "Sheep" is clearly polysemous: cattle of the islands, innocent victims. In the *mise en scène* the setting emphasized military elements: boots, old uniforms.[11]

La senora Macbeth and *Hamlet, de William Shakespeare* are hypotexts of the corresponding Shakespearean hypertexts, which can in turn be considered hypotexts of their so-called sources. Genette's taxonomy allows us to consider both Argentine modern plays as transformations, but it can be an oversimplification to consider that "the same" (Shakespearean) stories are set on stage. According to the chart in which Genette synthesizes hypertextual practices, the Argentine plays should be considered "transpositions," seriousness being what distinguishes this practice from parody (Genette 42). In both cases, but more noticeable in Cano's play, the use of language implies deviation, agrammaticality, solipsism. According to Derrida, nobody speaks more than one language, nobody speaks only one language (Derrida 22).[12] The conflict between two languages, in which one is necessarily more prestigious than the other, entails new, unexpected tensions in Cano's drama. Not possessing the language means a consciousness of colonial alienation or historical enslavement: "Argentine" characters use a faulty English to perform a *Hamlet* that is related to an armed conflict with the United Kingdom. On the other hand it can illustrate "irreverent" peripheral practices, the ones described by Waisman in the case of Borges (Waisman 202 ff.). Peripheral countries, like Argentina, may receive all influences without being particularly attached to any. According to Deleuze-Guattari grammatical acceptability is the first condition in submitting to social demands. If grammar is order and stability, trespassing upon it implies deterritorialization, stretching the language to its very limits, challenge (102). In the specific case of *Hamlet*, the topic of authorship, reinvented by Cano, illustrates J. Kristeva's ideas about the disappearing author, the interchangeability between the author and the addressee (190). Re-enactment implies infinite polyphony. Eventually, the topic is a new exploration of Stephen's theory about authorship as exposed in *Ulysses.* The alteration of chronology, the disintegration and combination of episodes and allusions to Argentina's contemporary situation, definitely build a new dramatic reality. I would like to finish quoting James Clifford: "What we may ask a member of a cultural community is not "'where are you from' but rather 'where are you between'" (97).

It can be said that all translated texts are somehow biased. Part 1 has shown a general tendency to weaken the impact of strong words. In translations intended to be mainly used in schools, or in a lesser degree, for stage purposes, these words have been bowdlerized or mitigated. Part 2 has displayed the freest interpretations: in them meeting Argentina's contemporary troubles implies recreating the texts, displacement, deterritorialization, recontextualization.

Works Cited

Allan K. and K. Burridge. *Euphemism and dysphemism: language used as shield and weapon.* Oxford: Oxford University Press, 1991.

Audivert, Pompeyo (Interview). "Pompeyo Audiverty el poder femenino." www. Lanacion.com.ar: 23 April 2004.

Cano, Luis. 2004. "Hamlet de William Shakespeare, de Luis Cano" Buenos Aires: edición digital.

_____. "Memorias íntimas" Teatro. La revista del Complejo Teatral de Buenos Aires. Buenos Aires, Año XXV, Nº 75, mayo 2004, p. 15-17.

Cela, Camilo J. *Diccionario secreto*. Madrid: Alianza Editorial, 1997.

Cosentino, Olga. Buenos Aires: Diario Clarín Revista Cultural No. 8, 7 June 2004.

Chamizo Domínguez, Pedro. 'La función social y cognitiva del eufemismo' <http://www.medtrad.org/pana.htm> Tribuna.

Clifford, James. 'Travelling Cultures.' *Cultural Studies*, Lawrence Grossberg, Cary Nelson, Paula Treichler, ed. New York: Routledge, 1992. pp. 96-112

Deleuze, G.F. Guattari, "Postulados de la linguistica." En: *Mil mesetas*. Traducción de José Vázquez Pérez, con la colaboración de Umbelina Larraceleta. Valencia: Pretextos, 1988. p. 81-116.

Derrida, Jacques. El monolingüismo del otro (o la prótesis de origen). Trad.de Horacio Pons. Buenos Aires: Manantial, 1997.

Gambaro, Griselda interviewed by Ñ: "El teatro de la herida absurda." Buenos Aires: Diario Clarín Revista Cultural, No. 8, 7 June 2004

_____. *La señora Macbeth*. Buenos Aires: Grupo Editorial Norma, 2003.

García Soriano, Justo y Justo García Morales, eds. *El ingenioso hidalgo Don Quijote de la Mancha* . Madrid: Aguilar, 1968.

Genette, Gérard. *Palimpsestos. La literatura en segundo grado*. Traducción de Celia Fernández Prieto. Madrid: Taurus, 1989.

Kristeva, Julia. "La palabra, el diálogo y la novela." *Semiótica 2*. Traducción de José Martín Arancibia. Madrid: Fundamentos, 1981, pp. 187-226.

Pacheco, Carlos. 'Hamlet y Lady Macbeth suben a escena, recreados'. www. Lanacion.com.ar.

Partridge, Eric. *Shakespeare's Bawdy*. London and New York: Routledge, 2001.

Ridley, M.R. *The Arden Shakespeare. Othello*. London and New York: Routledge, 1990.

Shakespeare, W. *Otelo*. Buenos Aires: Agebe, 2003.

_____. O*telo*. Traducción de Jaime Clark. Prólogo de Antonio Pagés Larraya. Barcelona: Océano, 1998.

_____. Otelo. Traducción, Notas e Introducción de Rolando Costa Picazo. Buenos Aires: Colihue Clásica, 2004.

_____. Otelo. Traducción de Jaime Collyer. Buenos Aires: Grupo Editorial Norma, 2000.

Waisman, Sergio. *Borges and Translation*. Lewisburg: Bucknell University Press, 2005.

Mr. Goodwill in *Rancho Grande*: Investigating the "Ghostly" Presence of Shakespeare in Mexican Cinema

ALFREDO MICHEL MODENESSI
Universidad Nacional Autonoma De Mexico

Though often staged in Spanish-speaking countries—and sometimes madly successful—Shakespeare has never been a frequent source for Spanish-speaking cinema, television or similar media. Practically no films have been made "straight" from Shakespeare, regardless of genre or country, and only sparsely have his plays been used in readily identifiable manner for film or TV adaptations, or even for recording performance in ways other than non-artistic video-taping of stage productions. Elsewhere I have ventured that, given "the relatively abundant production [of films "straight" from Shakespeare] in other European and non-European languages, the contrast is so sharp that one feels tempted to speculate upon reasons of historical/ cultural competition and resistance." The issue is worth exploring, and I wish to start precisely from an "oblique" perspective belonging in my preliminary work for a book project that aims at locating and discussing the presence of Shakespeare in the history of Mexican cinema. Ex/appropriations of Shakespeare into film with only a covert or tangential connection with Shakespeare may not be so wanting in Mexico, and identifying his "ghostly presence" in films made at diverse stages in the history of Mexican cinema might contribute some food for thought to the present book.

Among the *identifiable*, though not always *identified*, Spanish-speaking Shakespeare films are an Argentine picture seemingly based on *Romeo and Juliet*, directed by Arturo S. Mom in 1938; another, with the curiously inverted title *Julietay Romeo*, made in Spain in 1939 by José María Castellví; a "free" version of *The Taming of the Shrew* made in, and adapted to, Spain as *La fierecilla domada* (1955), directed by Antonio Román; *Macbeth Sangrador* (Venezuela, 1999), adapted locally by director Leonardo Henríquez; and two Mexican films: *Romeo y Julieta*, directed by Miguel M. Delgado in 1943, and *Huapango* (2003), made by Iván Lipkies, and co-written with María Elena Velasco, avowedly from *Othello*. Apart from being the closest to a "straight" adaptation from Shakespeare made in Mexico, the latter seems better known than the former among scholars nowadays, yet both equally illustrate not only the two paths that Mexican Shakespeare adaptations seem to have commonly taken, but also the directions that Mexican cinema has historically gone—nothing fancy: the paths of "town" and "country."

Mexican cinema reached a high degree of industrial development in 1943. That year also saw the release of several films that legitimized the artistic claims of the Mexican industry and its creative agents, and consolidated its legendary "Golden Age." Among them were two of Emilio "El Indio" Fernández's best: *Flor Silvestre* and *María Candelaria . . . María Candelaria*, Fernández himself and [cinematographer Gabriel] Figueroa were awarded major prizes in both Cannes and Locarno. . . . Surely the exotic quality of these rural tragedies contributed to their international recognition. But 1943 was also remarkable for the release of less tropical pictures dealing with complex urban subjects, such as Julio Bracho's outstanding *Distinto Amanecer* (based on a play by the Spaniard Max Aub), an indispensable reference for all the quality films to emerge from the Mexican industry in ensuing decades (Modenessi 2005, 228).

Like Fernández's major films, the less refined products of the Mexican industry had gone "country" from the start, especially in the form of *comedias rancheras* ("countryside comedies"). Their apparently harmless mythologizing of rural life quickly made *comedias rancheras* popular throughout Latin America and in Spain, as well as the most recognizably Mexican genre to date. Furnished with vernacular songs and picturesque landscapes galore; conventionally funny subjects; openly misogynist plots and flat characters; ready-made solutions to all conflicts; and a certain degree of verbal ingenuity, *ranchera* comedies display the complete, albeit vast, catalogue of national crafts and folklore: polychrome pottery, exotic costumes—regardless whether genuine or fake—gigantic *sombreros*, colourful ribbons on braided hairdos, *mariachi* and other local music, a great diversity—and use—of proudly Mexican spirits (a.k.a. booze), scores of *mucho-macho* role-models, and frequent bursts of popular wit through carefully calculated improvisations of songs and lyrics. In these comedies, all things foreign are a crime against national pride, and every sacred commonplace amounts to one and the same thing: every Mexican *must* keep the fire of "*amor a la Patria*" ("love for the Fatherland") burning bright and strong.

The success of the *ranchera* formula attracted the majority of popular actors, singers-turned-actors and comedians to star in such pictures—though not exclusively, as many of them were also featured in films with urban settings, again mostly comedies, that usually were as mythological as their counterparts. Melodrama abounded in both cases, too, with equal doses of rampant chauvinism. Despite some outstanding exceptions from the inception of sound, it wasn't until the 1940s that finer approaches and artists began to consistently deliver more complex films, ultimately resulting in remarkable careers, such as—to mention only the two best known—Fernández's on the "country" side, and Luis Buñuel's on the "town" corner—

Los olvidados (1950), for instance, remains the epitome of urban films in Mexico.

Delgado's parodic *Romeo y Julieta*, the sole instance of unabashed Shakespeare adaptation in Mexican cinema at the time and for decades to come, belongs emphatically on the "urban" shelf: its driving force and main actor, Mario Moreno, better known as "Cantinflas," comedian supreme, was and remains the quintessential representative of the *Carpero* tradition—a specifically urban phenomenon—in Mexican cinema. Although comedies set in urban scenarios were not infrequent, the town scene was more often associated with melodrama; and vice versa: the country scene was generally identified with comedy, in spite of the fact that *ranchero* melodramas were numerous and highly successful.

At first glance, *Romeo y Julieta* was intended as a vehicle for topical criticism of the foibles and presumptuousness of the Mexican upper classes through a "festive" version of a classic, in turn intended to provide its comic star with a propitious scenario to display his trademark antics while tackling one of the sacred icons of "high" culture—nothing unheard of in Mexican popular culture.

However, an additional and significant feature of *Romeo y Julieta* is that it not only aimed (half-heartedly, alas!) at mocking the universal (i.e. English-speaking) genius, but that it did so by expressly deriving from, and hence targeting, a specific Hollywood performance of the same play (George Cukor's *Romeo and Juliet*, released seven years earlier and fairly well-known to Mexican audiences), all in the midst and as part of the push that the growing Mexican industry made to compete with its powerful American counterpart, at the time hindered by its "war efforts." Summing up, the first, and until recently only, overt derivative from Shakespeare in Mexico can be described as an urban comedy (closer to farce?) that likewise avowedly and specifically responded to an American film made from the same source with evidently opposite purposes.

On the other hand, Lipkies' *Huapango*, made sixty years later and also avowedly deriving from Shakespeare, is a (border melo)drama that at first sight belongs in the *ranchera* tradition, but relates and responds in strong critical fashion to its own filmic roots, and to the ethics and politics therein, by means of a complex revision and subversion of the values and the mind-sets that predominated in the so-called "Golden Age" of Mexican cinema.

The formal features of that age are sufficiently inscribed in the description of *comedias rancheras* above. Its ideological contents may be summarized by saying that, for the most part, the "Golden Age" did not really examine the birth and development of a nation, nor, for that matter, did it sing the glories of human justice, equality or similarly high values. In it, the contradictions between individual and social ethics stay practically untouched in films that are at odds with epic, tragedy and sharp comedy, and by film-makers who prefer to be "gentle, tame, and meek" regarding politics and aesthetics. This age is full of films that look uncritically to the past, or in which the present is ideally identifiable with the past; it reeks of nostalgia for the *belle époque* of pre-revolutionary Mexico—the patriarchal times when Porfirio Díaz ruled—and is simultaneously in sheer denial that revolutionary Mexico remains very much Díaz's Mexico, only now by another name every six years. The "Golden Age" was rooted in semi-feudal *haciendas* where class and gender issues were artificially solved in vertical fashion through the generosity of the great and the gratitude of the small; then it flourished in semi-feudal farms and deprived urban sites where the old conflicts and solutions remained themselves. Among other important things, then, *Huapango* is sharply made to work against the grain of that age:

it is complex and finely crafted from Shakespeare's play—and in many ways, also *against* its grain.

Whatever happened during the sixty years between the release of *Romeo y Julieta* and *Huapango*? Over that period, no picture was produced that strictly acknowledged to have borrowed a plotline or basic narrative from Shakespeare. Still, several films are occasionally mentioned, mostly in conversation, that "remind" people of a Shakespeare play—or, to be *less* precise (and hence more so) that remind them of what that particular play "is about." Thus, the referent is often known only as a matter of cultural course and not from actual reading, let alone sufficient acquaintance with the relevant text, which renders many such references unreliable or misleading. A simple example is provided by a curiously recurrent but ultimately understandable association of Buñuel's *Él* (1953, co-written with Luis Alcoriza from a novel by Mercedes Pinto) with *Othello*, where the only true connection is that both feature a jealous husband. In other cases, the reference is merely topical—characteristically in titles relating to *Romeo and Juliet*.

Nevertheless, five of the movies either referred to me, or about which I have been consulted, deserve attention, and at least two of them perhaps careful study. The sources for most of them are no surprise at all: two may be associated with *The Taming of the Shrew* and another two with *Romeo and Juliet*. The fifth one seems worth exploring in connection with *Macbeth*. In what follows, I will only deal with the first two, with the hope, I repeat, that something in my descriptions may relate to notions such as "metamorphosis" and "intermediality" with regard to their Shakespearean source (or sources).

The pictures that may be associated with *Shrew* are Emilio Fernández's *Enamorada* (1946, "A Woman in Love"), co-written with Íñigo de Martino; and *El charro y la dama* (roughly "The Mexican Cowboy and the Lady"), adapted and directed by Fernando Cortés in 1949 from a story by Max Aub. It may be of interest, if not immediately significant, that both male leads were played by Pedro Armendáriz, a handsome figure and capable actor who spent a brief period in Hollywood. The two films fit the description of *comedia ranchera*, although the former is by far less formulaic.

In *Enamorada*, Juan José Reyes, a general in the Mexican Revolution (1910-1917), takes over the town of Cholula and rounds up its rich to collect war-taxes. In the process, Reyes has a long-winded, big-worded discussion with the priest of the town, a childhood friend of his, about the best and worst that religion and revolution can offer to the project of a new nation (a staple in Fernández's films). Reyes also learns that the daughter of the wealthiest man in town is soon to marry an American engineer, who asks for safe passage to Mexico City in order to purchase the wedding gown. Dumbfounded by the request but moved by the foreigner's depth of feeling, Reyes confesses that he has never really loved anyone.

Later, this blunt and brutally handsome General sees the refined and stunning Beatriz Peñafiel[13] (María Félix) in the street. Without realizing who she is, in manner closer to *R&J*, and after she manages to earn the right to slap him twice—and does—Reyes, deeply impressed and deeply in love, swears she'll be the woman he'll marry. The rest can be easily surmised.

Important details include that Reyes actually asks permission from Beatriz's father to formally see her, which the father cannot grant or refuse because *she* makes the decision not to ever let Reyes in *her* house. In one famous sequence she hits Reyes on the head as he puts his ear against the closed gate, hoping she'll exchange a few words through it. She doesn't get away unhurt, however, since he retaliates in similar fashion; as in the street, they are shown to be deserving opponents. During an increasingly heated conversation outside the church, they exchange instructive points regarding their origins and sundry views on life. The exchange ends as he violently pushes her to the ground, but, see, this is a *comedia ranchera*: aggression *doesn't* play against the grain of the genre.

Every night Beatriz resists opening her balcony to the recurrent serenading of Reyes, as she is increasingly interested in the brute, not only because she has been all along attracted to him and is rapidly "understanding major truths" about herself and her country, but also because he is likewise undergoing change. The very night Beatriz is to marry her alien fiancé, Reyes decides—clearly as a consequence of *his* re-education—to withdraw from Cholula instead of sacrificing his men (and women) to the overpowering government forces. And Beatriz, just before signing herself off to a life away from her land with the rich foreigner, and in no comedic mood whatsoever, grows aware of her real self as she accidentally yanks off of her neck the string of pearls he gave her as a final token of commitment, and rushes out of her safe home, torn between her past and present loyalties, to follow her real man, or rather, to walk alongside him, at the heels of his horse!, like a good "*soldadera*,"[14] towards the sunrise of revolutionary life—as usual, exquisitely photographed by Gabriel Figueroa.

All things considered, *Enamorada* isn't exactly a Shakespeare spin-off, but still a very interesting case of association with Shakespeare—to begin with, simply because it is so often assumed to be a more transparent derivative of *Shrew* than it actually is (and to a certain extent of *R&J*), and thus testifies better than the rest to the funny comedy of mistaken "reminds-me" sketched above. More importantly, it would be interesting to try and connect whatever bit of "Shakespeare" may be found in this film with its powerful hold on the minds of several generations of Mexicans (including mine). *Enamorada* is better known than *El charro y la dama* by inifinte far, as well as a fundamental contributor to the paradigms of its genre in mid-century Mexico, and to the consolidation of its main agents as the supreme myths of questionable but deeply enduring social and self-images.[15] The protagonists were already revered, but with *Enamorada* they absolutely defined the "romantic" Mexican couple of *comedias rancheras*. Emilio Fernández, already an outstanding figure in Mexican and world cinema, found in this intelligently nuanced, bittersweet *comedia ranchera*—as opposed to the rural dramas that had made his reputation inside and outside Mexico—the vehicle to be fully accepted and admired from every angle by high and low audiences alike. The many small things that make *Enamorada* both a quintessential *comedia ranchera* and at once a not-so "tame" generic film warrant further exploration. One simple thing to consider is that, being such a stronghold of putridly chauvinist nationalism, *Enamorada* should still be frequently associated—and though not so overtly, to a degree rightly so—with the "genius" from an "alien" culture. There is much more to sift regarding this film, of course, especially in connection with *Huapango*, as I hope to have shown elsewhere.

Instead, with *El charro y la dama*, more seems to mean less. Diana Henderson wonders why *Shrew*, a comedy "lacking the gendered inversion of power and the poetic complexity of Shakespeare's romantic comedies," is so often filmed: "more than eighteen screen versions of the play have been produced in Europe and North America. . . . What accounts for this frequent reproduction of an anachronistic plot premised on the sale of women?" She offers an answer from Michael Dobson's assessment of Garrick's *Catharine and Petruchio*: seemingly minor changes in the text "mute . . . the outright feudal masculinism of *The Taming of the Shrew* in favour of guardedly egalitarian, and specifically private, contemporary versions of sympathy and domestic virtue" (qtd. Henderson 2003, 120); and concludes that such versions belong in "a performance tradition that tames not only the "shrew" but also the text" (120). *El charro y la dama* belongs in the same tradition while aptly representing the weakest sides of *comedia ranchera*. For starters, therein the use of famous arguments usually responds to the laws of minimal effort.

El charro y la dama opens on a slapstick scene in which Patricia, the "shrew" (played by the Argentine beauty turned Mexican star Rosita Quintana) shreds her wedding dress while refusing to marry her sixth suitor, an American (played by another Argentine) who is one more in a list of boring foreigners that couldn't "tame" her. Her father decides to take her and her friend Clara (a name evidently evoking "Bianca") to his ranch in Mexico. They take a plane, then a train, and finally a horse-drawn wagon—a self-evident sequence of transport—as they approach a place increasingly unlike the foreign (modern and urban) milieu where the spoiled girl has spent most of her educational years.

After the wagon is held up by bandits, Patricia rides off in search for help and meets Pedro (a doubly obvious choice of name). It does not take long before sparks begin to fly—that is, they fight and hate each other. "At the (big) ranch" a homecoming feast has been organized, where Pedro will perform a trick: he will shoot a stick of molasses off the top of a dummy's head while in full gallop. However, Patricia dares him to shoot it off *her* head and then trade places. Pedro misses on purpose. It takes her four shots to hit her mark. Pedro responds by using his remaining three turns to shoot at only half the bar. Patricia faints.

That night there is a ball in their honour. Another contest is played; this time it is a match of wits involving the improvisation of verses ("*coplas*") to vernacular music. Whoever delivers the best *copla* to Patricia will win, but the shrew boldly cuts in to improvise her own set of derogatory rhymes against the *charros*. Pedro one-ups her again, and wins the contest by delivering a stanza chastising her for her impudence in dressing. She then sets him up by planting a medal in his pocket and accusing him of being "*El gavilán*," head of the highwaymen. In court, she proves him guilty. Pedro is sentenced to death by hanging, but she shoots the rope loose so he can escape.

While the men are out looking for him, Pedro returns at night to kidnap Patricia. Now it is the women's turn to head out and find her. That night and the next morning Pedro "tames" her by making her sleep in the dog house, cook and clean for him,[18] and by scaring her by means of a stuffed crocodile. Attraction grows. Patricia reveals that it was she who set him free. They kiss and promise to marry. However, back at the ranch, he is arrested again, due to her trickery. But word arrives that the real *Gavilán* has captured Patricia's father, seeking to deprive him of the ranch. Pedro and the *women* rescue him and, so, order (of a certain kind) is restored. When the family is leaving, Pedro and his servant Constantino hold up the wagon once more, "abducting" Patricia and Clara—though, actually, they are quite willing to go with the "bandits." The couples kiss. Patricia confesses that it was she who planted the medal in Pedro's pocket, and they ride off into the sunset (without the benefit of Figueroa's cinematography) while he spanks her for her knavery.

There is a simpler way to sum this up. Girl meets boy and they hate, and fight, each other constantly. Girl and boy fall in love, but they keep on fighting. The keywords are "game" and "play." Shakespeare's *Shrew* is itself a huge practical joke on Christopher Sly, where word-play abounds along with games husbands and wives, lovers and suitors play. The very notions of "courting" and "taming" and "suitors" are part of love-hunting, which is gamehunting—early-modern puns intended. But they are all *structured* games: the play-within-the-play remains the best metaphor to try and assuage the shortcomings of Shakespeare's script. Petruchio's game is planned and for the most part carried out according to plan. It is a game played with flexible but definite rules within a theatrical circumscription.

Patricia and Pedro, instead, resemble a couple of raw minds fighting it out; they don't so much act as they react to each other, bravado against bravado: "here is the 'two of a kind' logic that some critics . . . apply to Zeffirelli's film, arguing that this wild couple stands in opposition to the tame, mercantile society of Padua" (Henderson 2003, 123-24). The film's simplest gimmick consists in showcasing two stars fighting each other but ultimately falling in love—the same formula, say, in *You've Got Mail* (1998, dir. Nora Ephron). If *Shrew* structurally relies on "a theme and variations, the basic motif of a contest being repeated and modulated into different keys: a physical fight, the bargaining for a marriage contract, a contentious wooing, and an auction," it may be said that in *El charro y la dama* the idea of wooing as a contest is transformed into "power foreplay": the contests played in the film are sexually charged to the hilt.

Again according to Henderson, in certain *Shrews*, "the most telling cinematic innovation [is] a post-'sexual revolution' directness in emphasizing the erotic appeal of Petruchio's body as a motivation for Kate's conversion" (2003, 121-22). In *El charro y la dama* the male body is not overtly eroticized, but it is an essential paradigm regarding power.

Patricia assumes male roles and attitudes to be able to fight: in the tight ideological fabric of post-revolutionary Mexico, gun use was strictly a man's activity. In the genre of *ranchero* films it was less usual for women to sing: Patricia improvises intimate lyrics in her first rhymes, assuming a male role while simultaneously semi-subverting it, and her second rhymes are even more sexually explicit. In both, Patricia assumes a dominant, "male," attitude. But her trump card is sexually charged with feminine "charms." No *macho* can fight that—except Pedro, the only character sexually powerful enough to do it. He "tames" her by reminding her of decency and tradition, as well as by using imagery expressly opposed to hers, in order to "cool" the "heat" of her explicitness. His verses, while checking her sexuality, show that he is also overwhelmed by her: he literally loses his cool and can't deliver a closing rhyme.

At this point the score is one-all, then, not two-love: he *did* win the shooting contest, but she actually took the match of wits. Yet, the "empowered" Patricia is not about to let go of boy-toy. She declares against all obvious proof that *he* won the second contest and gives him his prize: a kiss. Thus, she privately reasserts her sexuality while publicly keeping the appearance that the male has won. Furthermore, she then frames him as being *El gavilán*.

So far, it may look as if the film were demonstrably dissident regarding its genre. But there are important limits to such assumption, namely, the same constraints that make it impossible for *comedia ranchera* to move away from (or even a bit to the left of) conservative nationalism. In the 1940s and early 1950s, Mexico would complete its rotation from Díaz's *Pax Porfiriana* towards the covert single-party, neo-feudal dictatorship that characterized it throughout the 20th century (and, by the by, persists). Both *Shrew* and *El charro y la dama* reinforce social hierarchies. This is needless to discuss concerning Shakespeare's play. But should we take the two central characters out of Cortés's picture, we would be left with a perfect portrait of what Mexico *ought* to be in the late 1940s: the world of *comedia ranchera*, as earlier described, a site for uncomplicated stories in rural contexts with a sort of modified pastoral theme and an emphasis on (dubious and very conservative) nationalistic values.

Enter this frame two very loud characters who are to fall in love, and conflicts are rendered black and white: men *versus* women, the high *versus* the low, the pure *ours* against the corrupt and corrupting *theirs*; there is perhaps racism, certainly classism, and a rampant struggle of nationalism vs. "*malinchismo*" (the Mexican word to signify lack of pride in one's country). But the movie stays true to its "spirit," its genre.

Patricia and Pedro's relationship is based on pestering and provoking each other. It is with the same brusqueness and fickleness that they kiss after one revelation, and decide to marry after that one kiss, as though the erotic build-up were too much for them to control. With the same volubility she then turns him in, and instead of escaping, he stays just so he can slap her twice. Their emotions are thus rendered conventionally acceptable, unproblematized by any scripting or filmic resource or effect. The film flows freely through a sinewy Mexican non-battle of the sexes. The men obstreperously dominate—albeit only nominally, since this world is thoroughly presented as a concealed matriarchal society. The would-be scandal is not that the men "dominate" their "native" women, but that *this* woman is as boisterous as the men, i.e., that Patricia decks it out decked in male robes. Yet it never becomes a scandal, both because she is an educated woman—necessarily belonging in the higher classes and hence expectedly, though wrongly, "wild"—and also because, as she puts it, in all honesty, she *does* want a husband, someone who will put up with her neurotic temper. All clichés apply: the braggart male huffs and puffs while the female underhandedly controls it all; behind every great man there is a great woman, etc. The epitome of this comes when Pedro tries to save Patricia's father, is captured, and then all men are saved by the townswomen—and yet Pedro takes credit for it. Such is the prescribed picture of Mexico in the 1940s and 50s: a model for ages to come (present included).

What Ace Pilkington says of Zeffirelli's *Shrew* may apply: "Petruchio's [Pedro's] world is an exclusively male one similar to the environment which Romeo must abandon in order to love Juliet. While Petruchio [Pedro] educates Kate [Patricia], she domesticates him, reordering his life as he is reintegrating her into the society which she feels has rejected her, and which she, in turn, has rejected. In fact, both the lovers have operated outside the bounds of society."[20] And so her back-talking is never outrageous, much less an apparently feminist statement. Adding to this is yet another device which creates a sort of detachment effect preventing dissidence in reception. "No one expects a movie star playing Shakespeare [to inspire absolute conviction], and the plays or films around them benefit from the air of unreality, the lowered expectations of believability" (Pilkington 1994, 172). Armendáriz and Quintana, stars of the movie, literally exist in a separate sphere where a woman can be found talking back. But neither of them is representative of the common man, much less woman. The spectator is left wishing to be the star, but resigned to do as the backdrop characters do. There is no tackling of class issues here: the way is paved for love to conquer all, in spite of the gap, for the gap may be relevant but "(never) mind the gap."

Finally, the movie roots for blind nationalism, a requirement of the genre. Patricia ends up with Pedro and not with a foreigner: she is Patricia del Villar, she belongs to the small town ("Villa[r]"), to *"la Patria,"* the father/motherland. *El charro y la dama* is set in a society closed to time and place, a Mexican Arcadia where the charro is king, the corn grows high and tequila abounds. The film ends up being an efficient two-hour exercise in comedic rhythm—something that the more able Mexican directors of the time learned to master through a sustained output of filmic work, partly due to a decrease in American production during World War II. But it does nothing to redeem its origins, let alone defy them. Despite promises of dissidence, in the end, the high-class woman/star, even she, who could, bows to the *charro*, a word that in Mexico historically signifies the most sinister sides of our social and economic structure.

Then again, in this Arcadia there are no economic issues. Whereas Katherine, as "an object of exchange between men"[21] is literally sold to Pertuchio, Patricia is just transferred. It must be noted that this action comes after father and son-in-law-to-be have a public conversation in which Pedro refuses to legally marry her, thus denying the economic exchange. Society is freeze-framed in a non-conflict world. And education is rendered expendable, a non-investment. At the end of the day, Patricia was merely biding her time until returning to *ranchero* paradise and finding the one who'll be able to put up with her naturally unnatural temper. As Morris puts it, *Shrew* "is still capable of raising heated debate when . . . performed on the stage, and perhaps this is because it presents with alarming directness the dichotomy which underlies all educative processes. On the one hand education is designed to liberate and bring to full fruition the innate capabilities of the pupil. On the other, it is a means of reducing the individual to social conformity through the imparting of approved knowledge and acceptable skills" (133). In the *ranchero* pastoral of *El charro y la dama* nothing *can* change. Transformation implies the loss of that unique state of "perfection."

Patricia went away a long way only to come back the right way to the right place. And then she and Pedro meet, fight, love, and end up together—and learn nothing (as neither do we?), except, perhaps, how to match two blown-up egos doing each other "double wrong." Alas, a spin-off sinking into the sea of missed opportunities. . . . But possibly a valuable lesson concerning a time and an industry that could but would not outgrow its own small world. Too bad Shakespeare usually affords something to learn from . . .

NOTES

1. The phrase "*rancho grande*" is part of the title and lyrics of a very popular Mexican *ranchera* (country) song from the early 20th century :"*Allá en el rancho grande*" (roughly, "At the big ranch"), which in turn served as the motif for a historically popular and paradigmatic *comedia ranchera* with the same title directed by Fernando de Fuentes in 1936. Since then, practically every Mexican has responded to the phrase as meaning "a paradigm of

my homeland: Nationalistic, proud, natural, and pure"—or something to that chauvinist effect.

2. Exception can perhaps now be made of *Sueño de una noche de San Juan* (2005), an animated film made in Spain from *MND*, directed by Ángel de la Cruz and Manolo Gómez.
3. TV versions have not been so wanting in Argentina; for example, *Romeo and Juliet* has been taped for TV several times, mainly from stage productions (e.g. 1962 and 1966 by María Avellaneda; 1971 by Francisco Fuentebuena); it was also "developed" into a full-length soap-opera in 2007, produced by Raúl Lecouna. A couple of peeks at the latter should make its when, its how, its whereto and its wherefore abundantly clear—and perhaps enhance your appreciation of Kauffman's film. Enjoy!: http://www.youtube.com/watch?v=z_mfOuw24s.http://www.youtube.com/watch?v=0SOZl jxELYk&NR=1.
4. Alfredo Michel Modenessi, "Cantinflas's *Romeo y Julieta*: The Rogue and Will," *Latin American Shakespeares*, ed. Bernice W. Kliman and Rick J. Santos. Madison: Fairleigh Dickinson, 2005, 239, n2.
5. In a paper on *Romeo y Julieta* delivered at "Shakespeare on Screen: The Centenary Conference," Spain, September 1999, and later in Modenessi (2005), I said I'd been unable to locate it, but this may soon cease to be the case.
6. Mostly according to Jorge Ayala Blanco, *La aventura del cine mexicano. En la época de oroy después.* Mexico: Grijalbo, 1993, 54-55.
7. Buñuel himself was not entirely free from giving *ranchero* melodrama a try, as witness *Susana, carne y demonio* (1951), co-scripted by Jaime Salvador, the screenwriter of Cantinflas's *Romeo y Julieta.*
8. For a fuller discussion of everything herein mentioned in connection to this film, see Modenessi (2005).
9. One of the pictures discussed below, *El charro y la dama*, may be somewhat excepted, inasmuch as the writer of the original story did at some point acknowledge its evident connections with *Shrew*.
10. An example is *Romeo contra Julieta* ("Romeo against Juliet"), directed in 1968 by Julián Soler. This was a remake, scripted by no

less than Buñuel's long-time collaborator Luis Alcoriza (among his finest is *Los olvidados*), of a 1953 film originally called *El inocente* ("An Innocent Man") that, by the by, if at all, would bear more connections with *Shrew* than with *R&J*. The other is *Tres Romeos y una Julieta* ("Three Romeos and a Juliet"), directed by Chano Urueta in 1961, which relates to *R&J* as much as an oyster bed to a futon.

11. An apparently frame-by-frame American remake entitled *The Torch* was released in 1950, also directed by Fernández, featuring Paulette Goddard in the lead (who also co-produced), with many members of the original cast, including the male star.
12. Armendáriz also played the central role in Buñuel's *El bruto* ("The brute" 1953), written by Alcoriza.
13. The names of characters are suggestive, as in many of Fernández's films: "Reyes" means "Kings," and "Beatriz," apart from reminding one of Dante's muse, seasons the "Beatitude" in it with some irony. "Peñafiel" bespeaks "solid (loyal) as a rock." In *The Torch*, Goddard plays the character under the name "María Dolores" ("[Our Lady] Mary of Sorrows"), a change that is possibly significant in a variety of ways.
14. That is, as just another of the mythical women who mythically accompanied the soldiers of the revolution, "served" them, and fought against the bad government as bravely as them.
15. It's hard to tell how endearing these paradigms remain, for although the more educated, urban, people in Mexico now prefer to think of those issues as something of the past, this self-referential opinion seems far from applying to the vast majority in a country with an alarmingly low level of instruction and safety.
16. A full discussion of *Huapango* (hopefully improving on the paper I delivered at the meeting of SAA in Washington, April 2009) is forthcoming in Spanish either as a chapter in a book on "Arts and Violence" to be published by UNAM in Mexico, or in the journal *Acta Poética*, edited by the Instituto de Investigaciones Filológicas, UNAM; it may also be soon published in English on line by the electronic journal "Borrowers and Lenders."
17. "A Shrew for the times, revisited," *Shakespeare, the Movie II. Popularizing the Plays on Film, TV, Video, and DVD*, ed. Lynda E.

Boose and Richard Burt. London and New York: Routledge, 2003, 120.

18. Similar actions take place in the aforementioned *El inocente* and *Romeo contra Julieta.*
19. Brian Morris, "Introduction" to *The Taming of the Shrew*. London and New York: Methuen (The Arden Shakespeare), 1981, 106.
20. "Zeffirelli's Shakespeare," *Shakespeare and the Moving Image. The Plays on Film and Television*, ed. Anthony Davies and Stanley Wells. Cambridge: Cambridge University Press, 1994, 171.
21. Natasha Korda, "Household Kates: Domesticating Commodities in *The Taming of the Shrew*," *Shakespeare Quarterly*, 47, 2, Summer 1996, 117.

Prospero's Books: An Intermedia Reading of Shakespeare's *The Tempest*

MARIA LUIZA GUARNIERI ATIK
CÉLIA GUIMARÃES HELENE
Universidade Presbiteriana Mackenzie

Peter Greenaway belongs to a group of filmmakers who do not adhere to the conventional forms of cinematographic discourse. To his education as a painter at the *Whalthamstour School of Arts*, he added other accomplishments such as the production of videos for television, the staging of operas and plays and the organization of exhibitions and installations, which, fused in his cinematography, reveal the director's hybrid vocation. Ivana Bentes points out this vocation when she affirms that the cinema appears in Greenaway as a virtualization of all the arts, especially painting, a kind of post-cinema form which the filmmaker/painter-videoartist-installer looks backwards to a 2,500-year-old heritage of images, painted, drawn, photographed, decorated in *sgraffito* or decalcomania, finding in the cinema and in the new technologies not a rupture with what has been done but a continuity. This structuring and encyclopedic eye hovers above any narrative desire (17).

Umberto Eco (Maciel, 2004, 6) stated that the encyclopedia is something like an "unlimited semiosis," comparing it to a labyrinth in web form, since any point may have a connection with any other. And it is exactly by means of those connections that one arrives at the concept of multiplicity, which is fundamental for the understanding of the director's work—the weblike structure.

In *Motivacoes pictóricas e multimediais na obra de Peter Greenaway* (*Pictorial and multimedial motivations in Peter Greenaway's work*), Rosa Cohen, discussing the filmmaker's aesthetic universe, corroborates Bentes's words, showing that it "has been characterized by the dynamics of the images escaping delimitations, willing to cross boundaries . . . to transpose elements across films" (24), weaving a network of references among films, stages, art galleries and museums, by means of different languages, transmitted in different ways.

Peter Greenaway's cinema is discursive rather than narrative and invites the viewer to an active participation before the work. It is a cinema that goes beyond the cinema itself, crosses it, in language and device, because it is in the streets, in the theatres, in exhibition spaces and on the Internet. The director's films no longer belong to the cinema, that is, to a specific medium, but are, actually, cross-media.

One can therefore affirm that the filmmaker expanded the cinema and emancipated it from an arbitrary organizational structure, which confined it to a rigid format and forced it into a narrative. One is no longer talking of a traditional and domesticated cinema but, instead, of a post-media cinema without predetermined formats, free to multiply itself through media and spaces.

Those who watch the film *Prospero's Books* (1991), a cinematographic re-creation of William Shakespeare's play *The Tempest* (1611), without having a previous knowledge of English director Peter Greenaway's other works, will find it difficult to immediately apprehend in all its complexity this product that blends art and technology.

Eschewing the literary bias of several directors in the process of adaptation of classic literary texts, Peter Greenaway does not reconstitute imagetically the narrative thread of the

Shakespearean matrix, but, instead, transfigures it, creating a mosaic of images, voices and texts. Our aim in this brief study is to demonstrate the imbrications of this mosaic, enriched with elements from other semioses, media or hypermedia, in their dialogue with the Shakespearean text.

The Tempest, the last play written by Shakespeare before he accepted the collaboration of John Fletcher, was performed for James I's court at Whitehall Palace and, probably because of its great success at the time, it opens the *First Folio* as the first of the Shakespearean comedies. Published after the writer's death, in 1623, due to the efforts of actors John Heminges and Henry Condell, the *First Folio* is the first collection of Shakespeare's dramatic work of a total of thirty-six texts in the *Folio*.

The plot of *The Tempest* consists in a story of vengeance, love and conspiracies that accompany the fate of Prospero, the Duke of Milan. Dedicating a great deal of his time to books, especially those of magic, he withdraws from the state affairs and has his dukedom usurped by his own brother, Antonio, who, in his search for power, begins to persecute Prospero aiming at destroying him. With the help of Gonzalo, a counsellor to the King of Naples, Prospero flees to a Mediterranean island with his daughter Miranda. Gonzalo supplies the vessel with provisions, clothes and books. On the enchanted island, at Prospero's service, are the slave Caliban, a creature half-human, half-monster, and Ariel, a servile spirit, who can be metamorphosed into water, air and fire. Prospero's main objective is to take revenge on his traitors. Twelve years later, Alonso, king of Naples, and his retinue travel for the wedding of Alonso's daughter Claribel. On their voyage back from Tunis, a great tempest causes Alonso's vessel to go adrift, forcing everybody on board to abandon the boat. The shipwrecked survive and find shelter on Prospero's island. They do not know, however, that the storm, caused by magic with Ariel's aid, and the voyagers' dispersal were part of Prospero's vengeance plans.

Even so, instead of subjugating his enemies, Prospero forgives them, thereby regaining his dukedom.

Peter Greenaway's film *Prospero's Books* is viewed by many critics as an eccentric or extravagant adaptation of Shakespeare's *The Tempest.* Although Greenaway's aesthetic artifact approaches Shakespeare's classic text with due respect, the images that appear on the screen do not have the function of reproducing faithfully the succession of events in the dramatic text.

In other words, the filmmaker visually transforms certain passages of the source text, superimposing images to actor John Gielgud's reading of the play's original version. Thus, the five acts of Shakespeare's text make themselves literally audible.

While Greenaway's earlier works consisted in a reflection on an artistic form, *Prospero's Books* is the first film where he brings someone else's argument to the cinema screen. The very choice of the film's title points at the procedure adopted by Greenaway in his rereading of the Shakespearean text, that is, the play is re-created starting from Prospero's "books." All of them have an "infinite or monstrous character" and, assembled, "make up a kind of fantastic library," an "abridged version of the 'Library of Babel'" (Maciel, 2002). Thus, it is from the description of the twenty-four fantastic books in the protagonist's library that the cinematographic discourse is constructed, visually transfiguring passages from the source text.

The artifice of cinematic animation and manipulation of images enables the books to acquire life on Prospero's enchanted island.

According to the director, the film, in its organizational process, was divided into Past, Present and Future: the Past corresponds to Prospero's long explanation of his history, the Present deals with Prospero´s various real-time plotting and the Future concerns those plans Prospero makes to guarantee the success of his dynastic ambitions for his daughter (Greenaway,

1991, 13). The narrated events which occurred in the first part re-appear in the two subsequent ones, deliberately resulting in an amalgam of memory and fantasy, by means of the superimposition of images.

To the visual reproductions derived from Shakespeare's text, images extracted from the canonical repertoire of western art history are added, composing a dynamic whole that encompasses and expands the various elements amalgamated in the source text: spirits, phantoms, witches, monsters, magical symbols and elements pertaining to the medieval universe, which are interwoven with the humanistic values and Prospero's early modern mentality and Gonzalo's utopian dream, that of the creation of an ideal community.

The books in this fantastic library function as instrument of both Prospero's isolation and his interaction with the outer world, in his double role of creator and creature. In Herbert Klein's words, "*Prospero's Books* is an ideal portrayal of cognitive and pragmatic change. The crucial precondition for this process is Prospero's dual role as writer and protagonist. Whilst the writer can only move within the world of the imagination, the protagonist can change the world by his imagination. Writing . . . is the 'condition sine qua non' for the existence of this world and the audience is constantly reminded of the fact that the production of a literary work is taking place by the image of a pen or by its scratching noise on paper. The activities of writing and imagining are located in *Prospero's writing cell*: a transportable box located within the library, his retreat where he can shut out the external world. In his writing cell there are also his books, which form his most important link to the external world and are also his instrument to control it. . . . Although Prospero rules over the island inhabitants with the aid of his books, he still withdraws to his writing cell and continues to write more books which fill up his library. Thus the books have a dual role as the instrument of isolation and of interaction, of total unrelatedness and at the same time, of connectedness. (1996, emphasis ours)

The twenty-four books shown throughout the filmic projection are described by Peter Greenaway in his work *Prospero's Books:* a film of Shakespeare's *The Tempest*, a composite of different textual modalities. Besides the film script of *Prospero's Books*, it presents an essay by the director on the film's creation process, fictional micro-narratives built around themes extracted from *The Tempest* and reproductions of Shakespeare's own text.

As for the structure of the filmic organization, different from what happens in most cinematographic adaptations, there is not a transposition of the chronology of the source text, that is, act after act, scene after scene. The sequence of acts and scenes follows the successive and chronological presentation of the twenty-four books that form Prospero's library.

Greenaway modelled the books making use of the technology of high definition television, which, according to Jorge Gorostiza (177-78), made it possible to superimpose three images at the same time or the texts which are being said about each one of the characters, in such a way that metaphor and reality can be seen at the same time. The director relates this narrative procedure, which he had already employed in *Death in the Seine*, to cubism, in which several different aspects of the same object are represented at the same time.

The books, introduced by means of an interplay of superimposed images and by a narrator's voice-over, during the narrative pauses, reveal themselves as an extensive compilation of Renaissance knowledge, which ranges from astrology to geometry, architecture, cosmography, and other sciences.

The fact that the books that Shakespeare's Prospero studies are mostly of magic and that it is from them that he derives his power has probably inspired Greenaway to conceive of the books in his Prospero's library not as ordinary ones but as living, magical (and at times even phantasmagoric) books in which colors change, liquids ooze and glow, sounds and voices are heard, three-dimensional objects can be seen to move and spring out of the pages, plants, animals and mythological beings surround the words, showing that books reflect all that exists "outside a library context" (1991, 107). For instance, as it is opened, the pages of the book called *A Primer of Small Stars* "twinkle with travelling planets, flashing meteors and spinning comets. The black skies pulsate with red numbers. New constellations are repeatedly joined together by fast-moving, dotted lines" (*Ibid.*, 17; 20).

They are books with which the reader can interact. As Prospero turns the pages of Vesalius' *Anatomy of Birth*, his "fingers appear to become covered in blood . . . the organs of the body become three-dimensional . . . then red ink floods the paper. There is the sound of babies crying" (*Ibid.*, 70). In *The Alphabetical Inventory of the Dead*, "a voice chants their names with a sonorous but rapid whispering monotone. . . . We hear the doleful scratching of a hundred pens and the deep tolling of bells" (*Ibid.*, p. 76). When you open the smaller books inside *The Book of Languages*, many languages are released: "words and sentences and paragraphs gather like black tadpoles or flocking starlings . . . accompanied by a great noise of babbling voices" (*Ibid.*, p. 96).

Three books are related to the natural sciences, among which we can mention *The Book of the Earth*, which is described as follows: "its pages are impregnated with the minerals, acids, alkalis, elements, gums, poisons, balms and aphrodisiacs of the earth. . . . With this book Prospero savoured the geology of the island" (*Ibid.*, 20-21). In it also, "when Prospero runs his thumbnail diagonally across the page . . . the page—and the book—ignite with a bright pink flame" (Ibid., 80).

A Harsh Book of Geometry is number six. It is a book bound in leather, with engraved golden numbers, which, "when opened, complex three-dimensional geometrical diagrams rise up out of the pages like models in a popup book. . . . Angles are measured by needle-thin metal pendulums that swing freely, activated by magnets concealed in the thick paper" (*Ibid.*, 20). Plans and diagrams also spring out of the pages of the *Book of Architecture and Other Music*: "There are definitive models of buildings constantly shaded by moving cloud-shadow. Noontime piazzas fill and empty with noisy crowds, . . . and music is played in the halls and towers. With this book, Prospero rebuilt the island into a palace of libraries that recapitulate all the architectural ideas of the Renaissance" (*Ibid.*, 21). Renaissance architecture is present in the film settings, in the decorative elements, in the columns that delimit the scenic space or, in other words, in the labyrinthine space of the island-palace.

The mirror images, recurrent in the director's works, expand the network of references. In *Prospero's Books*, Greenaway makes use of mirrors to reveal what goes on behind the camera, breaking, in this way, with the cinematographic illusion and with the narrative schemes of traditional cinema. Exposing the artifices of filmic language, he highlights, to the spectator's eyes, the simulacrum implicit in every representation.

The mirror images are recaptured in *The Book of Mirrors* and establish an enticing interplay between the real and the imaginary, the stable and the transient, the reader and his double, as can be observed in the following fragment:

> Bound in a gold cloth and very heavy, this book has some eighty shining mirrored pages; Some mirrors simply reflect the reader, some reflect the reader as he was three minutes previously, some reflect the reader as he will be in a year's time, as he would be if he were a child, a woman, a monster, an idea, a text or an angel. . . . One mirror simply reflects another mirror across a page. There are ten mirrors whose purpose Prospero has yet to define. (*Ibid.*, 17)

The image of the first mirror the spectator sees appears in the same water where Prospero is seen in the opening sequence of the film. The reflected image is not only that of Prospero but also of the shipwrecks imagined by him. In this game of reflections, a drop of water, shot in close up and slow motion, falls in a dark swimming-pool. Other drops fall, successively, alternating with the first credits, shown on a black background. Then, the first book appears, a *Book of Water*, replete with "drawings of every conceivable watery association—seas, tempests, rain, snow, clouds, lakes, waterfalls, streams, canals, water-mills, shipwrecks, floods and tears. As the pages are turned, the watery elements are often animated. There are rippling waves and slanting storms. Rivers and cataracts flow and bubble" (*Ibid.*, 17).

Concomitantly with the images of the *Book of Water*, the associations established with water, with Prospero's Roman bath, with Ariel's interminable urine jet (shown in the three phases in which this character is presented—as a child, an adolescent and a youth) and with the toy boat facing a storm refer us back to the opening scene of the Shakespearean text, in which one hears "a tempestuous noise of thunder and lightning" (Act I, Scene i) and the shipmaster and the boatswain enter, urging the mariners to "Bestir.Bestir" (Act I, Scene i, 1.4) because shipwreck seems imminent.

The verbal images suggested in Shakespeare's play, sometimes evoke, in Greenaway's intersemiotic translation, the storm and Prospero's desire for revenge, sometimes symbolize Prospero's forgiveness, as the good sovereign of the enchanted island. "The trajectory ranges from the overwhelming images, the vortex of superimpositions on the screen, to milder images, which approach the conventional narrativity of the cinema" (Vieira 78).

It was owing to the 24 books that Prospero was able to reign absolutely over the magical island during twelve years. The last book, *Thirty-Six Plays*, is given to Prospero by Ariel and is described thus:

> This is a thick, printed volume of plays dated 1623. All thirty-six plays are there save one—the first. Nineteen pages are left blank for its inclusion. It is called *The Tempest*. The folio collection is modestly bound in dull green linen with cardboard covers and the author's initials are embossed in gold on the cover—W.S. (Greenaway, 1991, 25)

In the film's final scene there is the following sequence: first, we read on the screen the dedication: "To the reader." Immediately following, the initials *WS* appear on the leather cover and, on a sheet of paper, the word "boatswain." We hear a voice that utters the word "boatswain." A voice-off refers us to the initial speech. "And this is the thirty-sixth play, *The Tempest*." Stripped of his duke's robes, Prospero solemnly throws the volume into the sea. Caliban retrieves the book. And Prospero frees Ariel.

All the books are closed and thrown, one by one, to the water. The acid explosions and the fireworks which visually compose the scene, represent the destruction and dispersion of knowledge. "The whole sequence has been accompanied by Prospero's magic music—orchestrating the destruction of the books" (Greenaway, 1991, 162). However, two books are recovered, the collection of Shakespeare's plays and a thin book, which was being written by Prospero.

Shakespeare's Prospero abjures magic and says that he will "break [his] staff" and "bury it certain fathoms in the earth" (Act V, Scene i, ll. 54-55) and that he will "drown [his] book . . . deeper than did ever plummet sound" (Act V, Scene i, ll. 56-57). In Harold Bloom's words, Prospero's gesture means throwing into the sea "the work of a lifetime," since the book was "the fruit of hard work, involving reading, reflection and practice, in what concerns the control of spirits" (811).

Greenaway's Prospero, in his turn, figures as a composite of his readings. His body is shown, in various scenes, covered with words, thanks to the visual effect of superimposition of screens. The written word symbolizes his superior erudition as well as an instrument of power which he possesses over his enemies and over the savage and illiterate slave Caliban.

The materialization of the written word can be apprehended since the first scene. The director presents the credits in two parts. In the opening scene, when Prospero puts on his magic cloak, the names of the actors and technical staff are superimposed on the image. A close-up of the cloak's embroidered cloth, in shades of blue, serves as a transition to the insertion of the remaining credits. Next, in a slow side travelling, the camera follows Prospero's steps, when he traverses an arched gallery, accompanied by his subjects. The film's title appears first, followed by the final credits. A new close-up of the cloak's cloth indicates the end of the credits. But, this time, the color blue changes gradually and the cloak acquires a reddish hue. At the end of the film, only the words *The End* are seen, in the middle of the image, and the reference to the author's copyright appears in small characters, in the lower part of the screen. (Bouchy).

The blue cloak and the red cloak serve, in their turn, to highlight the protagonist's dual role: Prospero the playwright, who acts as the author of the play staged throughout the film, and Prospero the actor, who, like the other characters, performs under the dramatist's pen and command.

> Prospero the writer (or dramatist) establishes a relationship between the image built by Prospero and Shakespeare's creation process. Resorting to the manuscript word, materialized on the screen, and its relation to the very writing process, the filmmaker shows in close-up objects such as the ink, the quill and the inkpot. (Vieira, 77)

With ink, quill and inkpot, Greenaway pays homage to the copyists of the Middle Ages while visually evoking the process of cultural transmission from past to present. The graphic richness of calligraphy is explored by the filmmaker in the very process of the construction of images.

According to Karine Bouchy, "Greenaway had a precise idea of the role he wanted to give to the manuscript letter in movement. It was for this reason that he needed a collaborator." Greenaway's meeting with Brody Neuenschwand, thus, allowed for the exploration of new filmic possibilities. The filmmaker wished to inscribe in the diegetic space handwriting similar to Shakespeare's. Neuenschwand's training in art history and his studies of manuscripts at the university made it possible for him to analyze and reproduce Shakespeare's hand. However, as Karine Bouchy points out, the only documents on which the calligrapher could be based are limited to some signatures, which is far from being sufficient to establish a style and a whole alphabet. But, for Peter Greenaway, the cinema is not a matter of reproduction, of realism or of authenticity. Shakespeare's writing was only a starting point to determine a graphic rhythm. It was even more important that this writing be legible since Greenaway's main intention was to explore the interactions among the movement of the strokes, the read word, the same word pronounced in voice-off and the image. So, in the form of an allegorical tempest of words, images and voices, Greenaway proposes an interminable game of puzzles, a labyrinth of signs in movement which leads the spectator to the discovery or identification of allusions, quotations, dislocations, words beneath words, one text beneath another text, images beneath other images. In this labyrinth, however, nothing is fortuitous, all the elements have their function.

A careful examination of *Prospero's Books* as a whole invites us to another relational reading. Beneath a profusion of freezes, of frames within frames, of a multiplicity of representational forms, there is a recreation of the Baroque pictorial universe in dialogue with inscriptions of Renaissance images. Denise D. Guimarães (65) points out that although the sculptural and architectonic elements, such as "the setting with arches, columns and domes," refer us back "to Renaissance constructions," "the film explores this environment in semi-obscurity, re-creating the Baroque *chiaroscuro*." As Guimarães (58) points out, this is a typical procedure of the postmodern aesthetic propositions, in their predilection for eclectic, disjunctive and parodic forms. The link between the two periods becomes irrefutable in the presence of the ambivalence cherished by the filmmaker, both in the technical rupture with contemporary ways of cinema making and in the deliberately intertextual composition, which brings a new dimension to filmic semiosis, imposing a constant dialogue with the other arts.

In Greenaway's characterization of Prospero, one can also observe the play between these two aesthetic languages. Prospero's face shows similar traits to those of Georges de La Tour's "Saint Jerome," resorting to the technique of Baroque *chiaroscuro*, while his garments resemble those of a Venetian doge, in this case, those of "Doge Loredan" by Renaissance painter Giovanni Bellini.

In the compositional process of scenes and settings, paintings by Botticelli, Rubens and Raphael Sanzio are transcribed by the filmmaker, with striking similarity, among other visual appropriations or quotations. In Florence Besson's words, "the tempest in Prospero's library is blown by the Boticelli winds (*The Birth of Venus*), the library itself pays homage to Michelangelo's Laurenziana Library, and Prospero's writing room comes from St Jerome's by Da Messina." In their turn, the Baroque canvases, ornamented with figures, flowers and fruit, "like those of Rubens in the Louvre on Maria de Medicis' life," function, according to Gorostiza, "to furnish the interior." (167)

Other imagetic influences also contributed to build the visual universe of *Prospero's Books*. Greenaway admits to having been inspired "by the magic" of filmmaker Georges Méliès as well as by George Lucas's film *Star Wars* and "above all by the images created by Cocteau for *Beauty and the Beast* and *The Testament of Orpheus*" (Gorostiza, 167).

Greenaway's film is an artistic object difficult to classify within the limits of a particular genre. It is the fruit of experimental work, which proposes the valorization of cinematographic adaptation as a "hybrid construction." In *Prospero's Books*, such construction makes possible the dissolution of the boundaries among the languages of different sign systems and supports, establishing a unique network of intertextual and intersemiotic relations. Thus, it is in this borderline locus that theater, cinema, visual arts, electronic technology, computer graphics and digital media converge to re-create, together, the drama of the Shakespearean Prospero.

Bibliography

Bentes, Ivana. Greenaway, a estilizacao do caos. In Maciel, Maria Esther (org). *cinema enciclopedico de Peter Greenaway*. Sao Paulo: Unimarco, 2004.

Besson, Florence. *Prospero´s Books* by Peter Greenaway (1991): reflections of/on Shakespeare´s *The Tempest.* International conference: "Re-writing/Reprising in lit. and the arts" Lyon 2, Oct.06. Available at: conferences.univ-lyon2.fr/index.php/reprise/reprise/paper/view/34/64

Bloom, Harold. *Shakespeare: a invencao do humano. Traducao de José Roberto O'Shea*. Rio de Janeiro: Objetiva, 2000.

Bouchy, Karine. Generique et Calligraphie. Le cas Greenaway/Neuenschwander. Université de Montreal / Universite Paris 7 Denis Diderot Texte inedit publie sur Generique & Cinéma, Jan.2008. Available at: www.generique-cinema.net/. . ./greenaway.html

Cohen, Rosa. *Motivações pictoricas e multimediais na obra de Peter Greenaway.* São Paulo: Ferrari, 2008.

Gorostiza, Jorge. *Peter Greenaway.* Madrid: Catedra, 1995.

Greenaway, Peter. *Cinema is dead, long live cinema?* Available at www.sescsp.org.br/. . ./20080326_202040_Ensaio_PGreenaw_y_CadVB3_P. pdf. This is an abridged version of the lecture on the future of the cinema, delivered in Utrecht, the Netherlands, in 2003, which was summarized by the author especially for *Caderno Videobrasil.*

_____. *Prospero's Books:* a film of Shakespeare's *The Tempest.* London: Chatto & Windus, 1991.

_____. *Prospero's Books*. England-France, 1991.

Guimaraes. Denise A. Duarte. Inscricoes renascentistas sob a "pele" barroca: uma leitura de *Prospero´s Books*, de Greenaway. In *Imagibrida:* comunicacao, imagem e hibridizacao. Araújo, Denize Correa. Barbosa, Marialva Carlos (orgs.). Porto Alegre: editorialplus.org., 2008.

Klein, Herbert. The far side of de mirror: Peter Greenaway´s *Prospero's Books*. EESE, 12/ 1996. webdoc.gwdg.de/edoc/ia/eese/cont96.html.

Maciel, Maria Esther. Exercícios de ficção: Peter Greenaway à luz de Jorge Luis Borges. *Agulha*: Revista de Cultura # 23-Fortaleza, São Paulo-abril de 2002. http://www.revista.agulha.nom.br/ag23 greenaway.html

_____. (org). *O cinema enciclopédico de Peter Greenaway.* São Paulo: Unimarco, 2004.

Mourthé, Claude. *Shakespeare.* Tradução de Paulo Neves. Porto Alegre: L&PM Pocket, 2007.

Shakespeare, William *The Tempest*, ed. Michael J.C. Echeruo. London: Longman, 1980.

_____. *A tempestade.* Traducao de Barbara Heliodora. Rio de Janeiro: Lacerda Ed., 1999.

Stam, Robert. *Introducao a teoria do cinema.* Traducao de Fernando Mascarello. Campinas, Sao Paulo: Papirus, 2003.

Vieira, Erika V.C.; Diniz, Thais F.N. "*A Ultima Tempestade*, uma traducao intersemiótica inserida na contemporaneidade," *Cadernos de Traducao.* vol. 1, n. 5, 2000. www.periodicos.ufsc.br/index.php/traducao/issue/. . ./428.

The Stage as a Page and the Stage as a Screen: Shakespearean Metamorphoses in Stefan Pucher's *The Tempest* (2007)

ANETA MANCEWICZ
Kazimierz Wielki University, Bydgoszcz, Poland

Among Shakespeare's works *The Tempest* is particularly appropriate to examine the themes of transit, transfer, and transition. The play exhibits the early Modern fascination and fear connected with sea voyage and newly discovered civilizations. It also exploits the intersection between science and sorcery in the portrayal of Prospero as a scholar and a conjurer who holds power over the people and the events on the island. Parallel to different forms of knowledge transfer: scientific, linguistic, or cultural, *The Tempest* involves various examples of magical transmutation, beginning with the eponymous sea storm, which sets off the entire action. Finally, the events in the drama continuously oscillate between calamity and good fortune, leading to the unresolved tension between comedy and tragedy. The play's finale is ambiguous if not alarming—Prospero's decision to return to Milan as a vulnerable old man leaves him at the mercy of his recent enemies. Thus, rather than closing the drama with an apparently happy ending, Shakespeare leaves it at the onset of a potential tragedy.

Stefan Pucher's stage production of *The Tempest* at the Münchner Kammerspiele, which premiered on November 8, 2007, reflects not only on transfers and transformations inscribed within the play, but also on metamorphoses and modifications involved in the process of Shakespeare's appropriation. The production adapts the source text into various forms: drama, performance art, film, and music—the multiplicity of media illustrates the wide range of Shakespearean appropriation and allows Pucher to contemplate on the issues of authority and fidelity, which are raised by each new version of Shakespeare's drama. The paper suggests early, tentative ideas for the discussion of media transactions and digital technologies involved in this production, with a view to formulating a more general theory of intermediality in contemporary performances of Shakespeare's drama.

The Munich adaptation has been highly successful with audiences and critics, confirming the status of Pucher as one of the most prominent German directors. The production exhibits typical features of his staging: the innovative use of popular music, the application of video art and the blending of pop culture elements. Pucher began his career cooperating with an experimental, media-oriented group Gob Squad, gaining the title of one of the leading German "pop-culture directors" (Carlson 186). Since the turn of the century, he has been recurrently staging the works of Anton Chekhov and Shakespeare, establishing himself as an inventive interpreter of classic works. His productions have been frequently invited to the Theatertreffen in Berlin, a theatre festival which features a selection of ten most ground-breaking stage works produced during a single season in Germany and Austria.

In 2008 *The Tempest* not only opened the Theatertreffen, but it was also recorded for the German ZDF-Theaterkanal, with Peter Schönhofer as a film director. A performance event was thus translated into a digital image. Applying Diana Taylor's terminology, a repertoire became an archive, with all the consequences of the medium shift (19-29). The transition from a performance event to a "videotext" reflects the reception patterns of the recent decades, with a video recording functioning as a modern equivalent of a text. According to Douglas Lanier, "Even as we have hailed the death of the monolithic text in favor of performative variants, the technological apparatus has encouraged this theoretical revolution the VCR has been subtly re-establishing, at another level, a new monolithic and stable "text" the ideal performance, recorded on tape, edited and reshaped in post-production, available for re-viewing" (203-4). Significantly, a digital recording has been the only form, in which I have been able to access Pucher's production; the medium has inevitably affected my interpretation of the play as a "videotext"—a fixed object, whose original spatial, temporal and political context has been removed. Instead of viewing *The Tempest* as a performance which insists on presence, perception, participation and memory, I have been "re-viewing" it as a "videoscript" which might be conveniently fast forwarded, rewound, paused, stopped and watched again an infinite number of times. Thus, the following analysis focuses on textual and video elements in the production, paying less attention to its performative aspects.

Pucher's *The Tempest* as a rewriting of Shakespeare's play raises questions regarding fidelity, originality, and authenticity, making apparent the relationship between drama and theatre. The director has commissioned a new translation from Jens Roselt, who has not only modernized the text, but also emphasized its metatheatrical elements. The translation underlines the role of Prospero as a director who manages the events on the island, while being constantly aware of the actors and the audience. Roselt's translation has been published in a book form, thus becoming a new version of Shakespeare's drama available to the German-language public. A bilingual edition of the play encourages the readers to judge the fidelity of the translation to the English text, as well invites audience members to assess the conformity of the staging to the script (the book might be purchased in the lobby of Münchner Kammerspiele before each performance).

Working with Roselt's translation, Pucher has extensively remade the text with the assistance of the dramaturg, Matthias Günther, creating a highly original version of *The Tempest*. The Shakespearean play has been cut, rearranged, expanded, and modernized. Pucher has included numerous elements from popular culture, bringing the Shakespearean script closer to the experience of the audience and underscoring comic effects in his adaptation. The identity manifesto of Caliban (Thomas Schmauser) is a song which parodies the heavy metal style of the German band Ramstein, portraying the protagonist as a contemporary beast, a modern rebel of the youth imagination. The dialogues of Stephano and Trinculo (Bernd Moss and Stefan Merki) allude to the silly rhetoric of television interviews and advertisements, poking fun at absurdist, nonsensical behaviour of the two characters. The comic effect is enhanced through their appearance and performance style—the two actors are dressed as Gilbert and George, performance artists residing in Britain, who became known for bridging the gap between life and art, and for using their bodies as "live sculptures."

The most striking reference to the process of rewriting the Shakespearean script, however, concerns the stage design by Barbara Ehnes, who frequently collaborates with Pucher, astonishing the audience with her imaginative projects. The moving walls resemble the pages of the book, which are turned with the change of a scene. The image recalls the authority of the Shakespearean text, which despite the growing popularity of the digital media continues to influence the performance and criticism of Shakespeare's work. As William Worthen notes, "Although the desire to reproduce either the dramatic or the theatrical circumstances of Shakespeare's plays has perhaps waned in the past century, contemporary discussions of Shakespeare and performance have in many ways not surmounted this turn-of-the-century problematic: the desire to authenticate performance as a reproduction of the text, of "Shakespeare" (36). Commenting upon the authority of the text in Anglophone theatre, Worthen nevertheless recognizes that the status of the Shakespearean script differs in productions staged in other languages. "Productions outside the English-speaking North Atlantic orbit have, on the other hand, long taken the lead in applying innovative scenographic practices to Shakespeare production" (33).

Pucher's adaptation ironically reflects on Shakespeare's status as a book in the English-language theatre (Marvin Carlson notes the indebtedness of the director to the British stage tradition, 182), where the notion of the original, authentic text sets the standards of performance for critics and play-goers alike. In the Munich *Tempest*, the characters are confined between the walls as if between the pages of the Shakespearean script—the walls at times frame or confine them, while at other times, they close upon them or push them into the back of the stage. The stage design not only continuously reminds the audience of the dramatic text underlying the actors' performance, but it also reveals conflicts and tensions between the page and the stage.

The authority of Shakespeare's book in the German theatre tradition is simultaneously confirmed and challenged. The act of altering and adjusting the Shakespearean text becomes one of the subjects of the production, with several episodes openly identifying Prospero (Hildegard Schmahl) and Ariel (Wolfgang Pregler) as artists reworking the Shakespearean script and directly addressing the audience. Similarly to Vanessa Redgrave, who was cast as a male Prospero in Globe Theatre in 2000, Schmahl plays the exiled Duke of Milan as a breeches role, investing her character with confidence and charisma. Pregler's Ariel is ironic and playful towards Prospero and other characters, and he enjoys more power than it is customary in the productions of *The Tempest*. For example, in the scene showing the intrigue of Sebastian (Jörg Witte) and Antonio (René Dumont) against Alonso (Walter Hess) and Gonzalo (Peter Brombacher), Pucher departs from the Shakespearean plot and allows Ariel to modify the scenario. After the king and the counselor have been suffocated with the pillow, it is Ariel who brings them back to life, informing the audience that their death would constitute a disappointing ending to the play.

Apart from manipulating the Shakespearean script, Pucher includes heavily edited video and film materials, reflecting on their application and function in theatre. The production's opening sequence, designed by Chris Kondek, shows the process of filming a sea storm and shipwreck in a blue box studio, with technicians pouring water from buckets on the actors to imitate the waves. The video material reveals the storm to be a creative, artificial act, introducing Prospero as an author and an artist in the play. More generally, the film intro reflects on the nature of illusion on stage and screen, in a manner similar to the intermedial projects of such theatre directors as Arianne Mnouchkine or Robert Lepage, who reveal the camera tricks of film makers to theatre audiences. In Pucher's production, the opening images of the sea storm continue to reappear throughout the play, mostly on a small screen in the living room, reminding the audience of the power of Prospero's artistic creation. At times, however, the video sequences take over the whole space of the stage, transforming it into an infinite sea and drowning all the protagonists in Prospero's magic.

The use of video images in the Munich *Tempest* is highly poetic, allowing Pucher to explore metaphorical and symbolic aspects of relationships between the protagonists, also when recordings function as flashbacks familiarizing the audience with the past events. When Prospero reminds Ariel of his imprisonment by Sycorax, the video sequence shows sadomasochistic, pornographic images, which suggest Ariel's dependence on Caliban's mother as sexual submission.

Furthermore, video sequences introduce colonial and political elements into the production through clearly recognizable images of colonial conquest (a reproduction of a historical drawing of an exotic island) and military aggression (images of tanks and soldiers). These sequences allude to traditional approaches to *The Tempest*, which has been frequently interpreted as a play about colonialism and aggression. In Pucher's adaptation these meanings emerge several times in the play, yet without dominating its overall interpretation. The Munich *Tempest* is primarily concerned with the relationship between the book, the stage, and the screen, with Prospero and Ariel directing the events on the island.

Finally, Pucher reflects on the presence of music in the Shakespearean drama by incorporating several songs and compositions into the production. The director has become known for his frequent and innovative use of music in theatre, also in his adaptations of Shakespeare's works, such as *A Midsummer Night's Dream* (2000), where "God is a DJ, and so is Shakespeare" (Carlson 185). *The Tempest* is particularly suitable for the inclusion of music, since, as Caliban observes, "the isle is full of noises" (3.2.131). In the Munich adaptation the noises are rendered by various music styles, such as pop, rock, hip hop, or heavy metal. Alonso in this production is wearing a yellow jacket with a large logo of Karl Kani, a fashion company associated with the hip hop culture, and the play contains several music performances, which are mostly entertaining, but which at times introduce elements of sadness and sorrow. According to Marvin Carlson, Gonzalo singing the John Lennon "Watching the Wheels" in the penultimate scene, "quite overshadowed Prospero's famous resignation speech as the coda" (193). Similarly to the application of video, the incorporation of music into the production has allowed Pucher to expand the meanings in the play.

Multiplying, blending and confronting diverse media in his adaptation, Pucher achieves several aims. The Munich *Tempest* evokes familiar experiences and memories in the German audience, relying both on comic effects and nostalgic notes. At the same time, the director engages in the questions of authority and fidelity, which continue to shape the performance and study of Shakespeare's dramas. In the Munich *Tempest* intermedial transactions become the very subject of the play, showing a way in which performances may "function as vital acts of transfer, transmitting social knowledge, memory and a sense of identity" (Taylor 2-3).

Works Cited

Carlson, Marvin. *Theatre is More Beautiful than War. German Stage Directing in the Late Twentieth Century*. University of Iowa Press, Iowa City, 2009.

Lanier, Douglas. "Drowning the Book. *Prospero's Books* and the textual Shakespeare." *Shakespeare, Theory and Performance*, ed. James C. Bulman. Routledge: London and New York, 1996. 187-209.

Pucher, Stefan and Peter Schönhofer. *The Tempest*. A ZDF-Theaterkanal recording, 2008.

Shakespeare William, *The Tempest*, ed. Jonathan Bate and Eric Rasmussen. Modern Library, New York, 2008.

Taylor, Diana. *The Archive and the Repertoire. Performing Cultural Memory in the Americas*. Duke University Press, Durham and London, 2003.

Worthen, William *Shakespeare and the Authority of Performance*. Cambridge University Press, Cambridge, 1997.

Celebration of Colonial Practices in *The Tempest*

CHINNADEVI SINGADI
E.F.L.U., Hyderabad

We have for long deified Shakespeare as the great universal thinker whose works intrinsically have a human side to them. We have unwittingly allowed Shakespeare, the imperialist, to dominate our conscience for centuries in the guise of the universal artist, the humanist artist and so on and so forth. We have spent centuries loving a man who had only all the while been sneering at us, calling us names and having a good laugh.

No matter how hard Shakespeare's supporters might try to argue otherwise, Shakespeare and the postcolonial must cross roads. Brian Vickers in *Appropriating Shakespeare* begs for Shakespeare to be read in his "proper" place. He deplores the tendency of the adherents of postcolonialism to reduce *The Tempest* to "an allegory about colonialism" (242). But I'd like to ask, "Do we have a choice?" *The Tempest* makes more sense when read in tandem with the history of colonialism than otherwise. That itself speaks volumes. In this paper I seek to explore the various ways in which Shakespeare celebrates colonial practices in *The Tempest.*

It is now an established fact that *The Tempest* is based on true events. The origins of *The Tempest* are clearly traceable to one particular moment in the history of colonialism. In 1609 an expedition led by Sir Thomas Gates set sail to the Americas to found more colonies off the coast of New Carolina. *The Sea Ven-*

ture, the ship that carried them wrecked on the coast of Bermuda. The crew survived the crash. One of them, William Strachey, went on to publish an account of his experience on the high seas titled *True Repertory of the wreck and redemption of Sir Thomas Gates Knight, July fifteenth, sixteen hundred and ten.* From the historical resonances found in *The Tempest* one can claim without doubt that Shakespeare had access to Strachey's story ("The Sceptured Isle"). That Shakespeare had also read Montaigne's *Of Cannibals* is evident from the text itself: one of the characters quotes Montaigne. These connections by themselves, I know, are not enough to label Shakespeare an imperialist.

Racial difference is at the centre of several of Shakespeare's plays, especially *Othello*, *The Merchant of Venice* and more blatantly *The Tempest.* The fact that Caliban's mother was dropped on the island by sailors suggests that Caliban could have been genetically a North African (Lie 26), a "vile race" according to Miranda. Caliban's savage appearance is by no means Shakespeare's attempt at comic relief: people of Shakespeare's time, actually believed natives to be so. The natives were seen as savage and powerful, meagrely dressed yet demonstrating no shame whatsoever. Shakespeare's Caliban is a reflection of the attitudes and beliefs of the late 16th and 17th century England, about the natives of distant parts of the world. Any description of the natives focused predominantly on their nakedness and physical prowess: 'They go all naked, the men covering no part of their body but their yard, upon which they wear a gourd or piece of cane, made fast with a thread about their loins, leaving the other parts of their members uncovered, whereof they take no shame" (Hakluyt 108).

The nakedness of the men clearly indicated that they clearly belonged outside the constraints of a civilized society. They looked like sexual objects lacking the restraint of a civilized being and capable of acting on impulse at any moment. So then it is taken for granted by Prospero, by Shakespeare and by his audience that Caliban of course must have attempted to rape Miranda. There simply could not have been a different opinion. Centuries later Doctor Aziz in E.M. Foster's *A Passage to India* experiences the same ordeal.

Kim F. Hall in a chapter entitled "Dramas of Alliance and Trade" in her book *Things of Darkness: Economies of Race and Gender in Early Modern England* states:

> The text itself locates Caliban on one side of a binarism in Prospero's final pronouncement on Caliban, "this thing of darkness I / Acknowledge mine," [5.1.143] and in clearly marking him as a slave who is associated with darkness and dirt: "thou earth" [1.2.31]. Caliban functions as a "thing of darkness" against which a European social order is tested and proved. (142)

Caliban is the original inhabitant of the island; its "first king," he tells Miranda. When Prospero, the Duke of Milan, having been dislodged from the throne by his own brother arrives on the island with his daughter Miranda, it is Caliban who educates them about the secrets of the island. Sadly, in return, Prospero enslaves Caliban and proclaims himself the king of the island. Caliban bemoans:

> This island's mine, by Sycorax my mother,
> Which thou takes from me. When thou camest first,
> Thou strok'st me and made much of me, wouldst give me
> Water with berries in't, and teach me how
> To name the bigger light, and how the less,
> That burn by day and night. And then I loved thee
> And showed thee all the qualities o' the isle
> The fresh springs, brine pits, barren place and fertile.
> Cursed be I that did so! All the charms
> Of Sycorax, toads, beetles, bats, light on you!
> For I am all the subjects that you have,
> Which first was mine own king. And here you sty me
> In this hard rock, whiles you do keep from me

> The rest o th' island. (1.2.33)

This speech by Caliban is nothing less than a preview of the story of Colonialism. Prospero believes Caliban to be a lesser being. This is quite evident from the fact that Miranda teaches him language, teaches him the ways of the "civilized." And of course Caliban benefitted: "You taught me language and my profit on't / Is, I know how to curse." (1.2.34) Caliban was bestial, and Prospero God-like, and so Caliban by all means deserved to be enslaved by Prospero. There is also evidence within the text that Caliban and Ariel have been subject to physical abuse by Prospero.

Now let's go nearer the text. Even as we get to the 'Dramatis Personae' the stink begins to rise. We see Caliban described as "a savage and deformed slave" while his name itself is a near anagram of 'Cannibal'. Clearly from the very outset Caliban was meant to be representative of the lesser mortals. The true nature of Caliban's deformity does not come through anywhere in the play. Prospero concedes, with much reluctance, that he is human:

> Then was this island—
> Save for the son that [Sycorax] did litter here,
> A freckl'd whelp, hag-born—not honour'd with
> A human shape. (1.2.29)

Trinculo cannot decide what Caliban is: "What have we here? A man or a fish? Dead or alive? A fish: he smells like a fish." (2.2.72) He goes on to refer to him as a "dead Indian. Legg'd like a man, and his fins like arms!" (2.2.72) But soon he too concedes: "this is no fish, but an islander." (2.2.72)

To Stephano, Caliban is "some monster of the isle with four legs." (2.2.74) He thinks, "if I can recover him, and keep him tame, and get to Naples with him, he's present to any emperor."(2.2.74) Note the use of the word "tame." Also note that both Trinculo and Stephano secretly wish to take this prize catch home with them: one to put him on display and make money (2.2.30) and the other to please his king.

Stephano and Trinculo repeatedly refer to Caliban as "monster." In Shakespeare's times the term "monster" generally referred to any "abnormality", usually manifested in "outsized proportions." Sadly, Caliban is not just "a savage and deformed slave." He is also referred to as "beast," "villain," "slave," "tortoise," "filth," "monster," "cat," "fish," "dull thing," "thing of darkness," " a freckl'd whelp," "dirt," "earth," "servant," "dead Indian,"—the list is not complete yet! And yes, Caliban is also a "shallow monster," "credulous monster," "perfidious monster," "drunken monster," "puppy-headed monster," "scurvy monster," "abominable monster," "ridiculous monster," "howling monster," "ignorant monster,"—there must be more of these; I just lost count. Is this not racial slur? Is this not the language used to dehumanize someone; to demean someone; to show someone low? Does this list from Shakespeare not qualify for a classic example of the underpinnings of the Oriental discourse which "[a]long with all other peoples variously designated as backward, degenerate, uncivilized, and retarded, [viewed] Orientals . . . in a framework constructed out of biological determinism and moral-political admonishment . . . [h]aving in common an identity best described as lamentably alien." (Said 207) And come to think of it India's ace spin bowler Harbhajan Singh almost lost his job for having supposedly called his Australian counterpart Andrew Symonds a "monkey". What Harbhajan said is actually "*maa ki* . . ." What the Western world does not understand is the fact that it is common for Hindi speakers in India to use the abusive term "*maa ki* . . ." which sounds more or less like "monkey," and the lip movement is very much the same (captured on camera in Harbhajan's case). The literal translation of "*maa ki*. . ." would be "your mother's . . ." the trailing off being an obscene reference to her genitals. In the Indian context "monkey" as an abusive term is unheard of, except usually as a tease word among children. It is surprising for most Indians to learn that in the Western world "monkey" is a far more serious term of abuse than the Indian "*maa ki. . . .*"

Prospero takes pride in his books. Nay, it's Shakespeare taking pride in the English language. The repeated references to language and books in the play help underscore the superiority of the English over the natives. Why else would Shakespeare have Ferdinand say, "My language? Heavens! / I am the best of them that speak this speech." (1.2.38) I would like to think that here Shakespeare is talking more for himself than for Ferdinand and rightly so because as Edward Said points out, "every European, in what he could say about the Orient, was consequently a racist, an imperialist, and almost totally ethnocentric." (204)

There is no denying that Shakespeare is one of the greatest writers that England has ever produced. In fact according to a recent BBC survey Shakespeare stands 5th among the greatest Britons ever. Fair enough! But how does one react to a statement like, "A single shelf of a good European library is worth the whole native literature of India and Arabia?" That's Lord Macaulay, at his egoistic best. More recently an Indian actress was called "a Paki," "a Poppadam" and what not on a reality show in the UK. Shakespeare *Khush Hua!* Shakespeare is pleased!

Works Cited

Hakluyt, Richard. *Voyages and Discoveries.* London: Penguin, 1972.

Hall, Kim F. *Things of Darkness: Economies of Race and Gender in Early Modern England.* New York: Cornell U. P., 1996.

Lie, Nadia, and Theo D'haen. *Constellation Caliban: Figure of a Character.* Atlanta: Rodopi, 1997.

The Sceptured Isle: Empire, Episode 19, Bermuda and Shipwrecks, BBC Radio (October 10, 2005), <http://www.bbc.co.uk/radio4/ history/ empire/ episodes/ episode_19.shtml.>

Said, Edward W. *Orientalism.* New York: Vintage, 1979.

Shakespeare, William. *The Tempest.* Kayedreams, 2009. <http:// www. books.google.co.in>

Vickers, Brian. *Appropriating Shakespeare: Contemporary Critical Quarrels*. New Haven: Yale U. P., 1993.

Romeo and Juliet: A Tragedy Re-Told in the Shanty Towns of Rio

ELIZABETH S. RAMOS
Universidade Federal da Bahia, Brazil

In 2007, the film *Mare—Nossa Historia de Amor* (*Mare—our love story*) was launched in Brazil having Lucia Murat as the director. The trailer, the teasers in the Internet, and the ads in the newspapers referred to it, at that time, as "Another Romeo. Another Juliet. Another love story," and also as "Lúcia Murat's Romeo and Juliet." Such calls made it clear that among the several possible interpretations of a work of art, the audience would come across one particular re-writing.

Lucia Murat, a former journalist, a political activist during the Brazilian dictatorship period in the 70s, and a classical ballet graduate, shifts the Shakespearean lovers to the shanty towns of Maré, in Rio de Janeiro, in the 21st century, involving the drama in the mantle of crime, drug traffic, and urban violence so frequently found in many metropolitan areas around the world these days. The conflict between the Montecchios and the Capulets is re-written in a war between two factions which dominate the drug traffic in the community of Maré. Analídia, the "other Juliet," is the daughter of the traffic leader who is in jail, and Jonathan, her "Romeo," is the brother of the opposing faction leader. The two lovers are separated by an environment of extreme violence, and find in the community dance group a refuge for their dreams, love, art and the possibility of a decent life, away from criminality. The film turns the Elizabethan play into a musical, depicting an environment where dance practices are the only possibility for fascination, and freedom not only for the lovers, but for the youth of these fictionalized slums.

Right at the beginning, along the seven long minutes of the film opening, Vinicius D'Black, the actor who interprets the protagonist Jonathan, sings a hip-hop hit—*Favela*—which means 'shanty towns' in Portuguese. All along, the camera moves through the alleys of Maré, where the dance group moves rhythmically, in different settings. The song refers to icons of Brazilian music—Sinhô, Candeia, Noel, Cartola—and the song chorus sets the scene: "Go and tell her that Rio de Janeiro is all a set of shanty towns." "Go and tell her that the song I sing comes from the shanty towns."

The breaking from the Shakespearean canon and from the intellectual elite who ultimately claims ownership over the play is clearly announced. Sacralization of the myth of authorship is bound not only to the English source; it is shared with recognized composers in the reception culture. Lucia Murat appropriates herself of the previous text, shifts it and re-signifies it into new characters inserted in another setting, time, language, permeated by other values, decoupling the source-work of its traditional value.

In one of the takes that follows, still in the opening of the film, the camera goes through a wall covered by graffiti, where one reads: "Art is what the world will turn itself into. Not what the world is now." Here, interpretation and creativity get intertwined in the expression 'turn into', leading the audience back to the re-signifying of the 16th century play, and to the future possibility of social transformation through the arts. In fact, despite the heavy scenes of violence, the film gradually builds up in the spectator the hope for the triumph of an energetic dancing youth over the rule of crime. Such hope is often built through dialogues and statements. When Analídia, the new Juliet Capulet, refuses to visit her father in jail, she says: "I've got no obligation to visit an outlaw in jail." She also refuses marrying her father's second man in traffic—the metamorphosed Paris—by saying: "I don't want to marry a criminal. I am not marrying a criminal"—statements which break with the paternal authority of the 16th century seen in Shakespeare's *Romeo and Juliet*.

The prohibition of a woman to act on the Elizabethan stage gives room to the character of Analídia, whose integrity, determination, and female dignity are expressed by her vigorous dance movements on the narrow alleys of Maré, where young men pass by casually holding rifles and pistols. Here, the Renaissance paternal authority is shifted to the law imposed by the Red and the Blue factions of drug trafficking which fight for the control of the actions in the area, defining what is acceptable and what is prohibited.

Romeo Montecchio is shifted to Jonathan, the community MC, whose dream is to have his CD released. Divided between his two older brothers—Paulo, a peaceful and idealist worker, who enjoys singing *samba* songs with his friends in his spare time, and Dudu, the adopted brother, leader of the Blue faction, which also fights for the drug traffic control in the slums—Jonathan lives the dilemma of accepting or not the help of his transgressing brother who promises to financially support his career with money earned from drug dealing.

Thus, the migration of signs and canonical resources, reconfigured into the mass culture in *Maré, nossa história de amor*, brings the themes of *Romeo and Juliet* closer to the spectator, supplementing and revitalizing the canonical work of art, by presenting to the audience a universe which is much closer to their own issues, allowing the public to seek "in the walls of their confinement . . . their mental images of the world" (Santiago, 125). Those, who have traditionally been excluded from the live performances carried out in fancy play houses, can find themselves as cosmopolitan beings in contact with re-readings of canonical artistic expressions, historically limited to the rich and well educated cosmopolitan individuals. Therefore, artistic productions can and must be enjoyed by a greater public, and may be "delivered to the contemporary consumer in his/her contemporaneity." (Santiago, 116)

The change in perception generates a new approach to translated literary works, leading us to understand that if a work of art is part of a tradition, it is alive and open to transformation by means of different interpretations and different intertextual dialogues, which expand into multiple readings. In a paradoxical move, the translator undresses the work of art of its sacred mantle and popularizes it, even though the removal of such mantle resulted precisely from the recognition of the aura of sacralization. Respect and recognition motivate the translation.

> The work of art loses something when it is technically produced and reproduced, but it acquires, as a consequence, the infinite places and contexts of its reproduction. And, if it loses its cult value, it acquires another function, adopting a non-specialized social practice. (Santiago, 114)

Mare, nossa história de amor keeps its theme tied with the play which originated it, bringing traces of such precedence, even though, simultaneously, erasing them. The shifting of the previous idea implies, necessarily, forgetting, even under the mantle of the debt. Here, I recall Roland Barthes when in *S/Z*, he reminds us that it is precisely because we forget that we read.

With her filmic re-reading, not only Murat confirms the plurality of meanings of cultural productions, but also endorses the non-existence of the so-called unique and crystallized meaning which the critics, for instance, try to attach to canonical works of art. The film director affirms in an interview: "I cannot deny that the technical rigour of classical dancing has always fascinated me. But life has also shown me that the same rigor can be found in the set of drum players of *Mocidade Independente*, in a Broadway show or in a good *Swan Lake* performance." The film maker thus decouples the concepts of originality and quality of the work of art, and confirms that the demands from the critics and other *patronage* groups, who define what should be culturally accepted, are based on subservience and in the erasing of the translator's point of view—when faced with the "purity" and the "truth" of the "unreachable" "original" text. Such expressions underline cultural inequality and, simultaneously, the subalternity of translation. The resistance to adaptations of canonical works reflect a remainder of the beliefs which held true in the 16th century, when the minimal interpretation unit was similarity, that is, the idea of an origin coupled to truth, ignoring that the beginning always results from a choice on the part of the interpreter in light of the unfinished feature of the act of interpretation, a feature which also led, the canonical William Shakespeare to adapt most of his plays. After all, his *Romeo and Juliet* has its roots in the 3rd century Greece, goes on to the Italian Renaissance, and gets to the English poet Arthur Brooke in his poem *The Tragical History of Romeo and Juliet*, with the objective of alerting the youth to the need for controlling their impulses, in order not to be overwhelmed by passion.

I refer to Gilles Deleuze, in his *The Logic of Sense*, when he claims that the precedent work, in its condition of original, should not grant it a *status* of fundament. The feature of uniqueness of the source-text will also apply to the reproduced text, since each translation will build "its own" reproduction. The model defined by the source-text will never be copied, for translation or re-creation will be built at another place of reception and production. In its position of a false suitor, it will have to kill the model, so that it can survive and, because it turns out a criminal, it will never be covered with the original's aura of sacralization, intrinsic to the perennial model, the truth, the origin, and image of perfection. The translated work does not want the aura, it does not intend to be a faithful copy. Its value lies in being another work of art, re-created out of a process resulting from a critical plunge into the source-text, inserted in another milieu, and sometimes through another medium. In the case of her re-reading of *Romeo and Juliet*, Lúcia Murat herself confirms that "any attempt to simply copy the rigor of the high brow culture would fatally result—more so for those who enjoy and are experts in dancing—in the ridicule." Thus, by removing from the previous text its aura of an unreachable work for the monolingual and excluded reader/spectator, translation takes away from the original its feature of supreme and sole truth, in order to deliver the new text with other looks to all of those who wish to get in contact with it. However, translation does that without fully breaking away from the text which came before. There will always be some kind of tie, to a lesser or greater extent, between the source and the translated text. In the case of interlingual translations of literary texts, for instance, the tie between the source-text and its translation is much greater than in intersemiotic translations of literary texts into film.

The task of the translator is thus performed on a palimpsest, that is, translation is re-written over the traces of a manuscript which has been washed and scraped. That does not imply though that a translated text will be less original and unique. The themes of violence and death are not only present in *Maré, nossa história de amor*. They also permeate the play *Romeo and Juliet*. Violence in Maré is apparently worse because it is part of our daily lives, making daily news on TV and in the newspapers. As one of the characters of the film puts it, after watching the *Romeo and Juliet* ballet on a DVD danced to the sound of Prokofiev: "In the past, killing was at the point of a sword. Today, it is at the point of a gun."

Once the long presentation of the film ends, and the audience is already acquainted with the re-signifying features of space and culture, the chorus of rappers announces the prologue of the Shakespearean translation: "Our love story begins in a funk dance . . . eternal love born in the sparkle of an instant. . . . Trusting the immortality of the actor. Trusting the immortality of love." Amidst an audience who dances to the sound of a pregnant funk singer, the film spectator sees young men also dancing while holding in their hands different kinds of guns as if they were soda glasses. In this scenario, Jonathan, the DJ of the evening, spots Analídia on the dance floor. Fascinated, he goes down to dance with the girl. Indifferent to the eyes of the others and to the music, they turn round and round, plunged into each other's eyes, in a profound state of fascination. The scene of passion on the screen is shown in suspension over the previous scene. Only silence and fascination involve the loving couple, who is suddenly drawn apart by armed members of both factions, in a mix of street dance, *capoeira* and martial art movements.

The balcony where the two lovers meet after that first encounter on the dance floor is Analidia's primitive terrace of an unfinished construction of a small house in the area. She breaks through the security control of the Red faction, and runs down to Jonathan. The chorus of rappers announces, then, that the two lovers "live in the limits between fear and the desire to love."

By forming a dance group made of several dance groups in Rio de Janeiro, thus working with the Brazilian ethnical and cultural diversity, the film re-configures William Shakespeare's tragedy. Just as the English playwright brings to his play "plenty of information on Italy, Verona, social habits and many other details which are useful for the building up of the play"[3] (Heliodora, 124), Lucia Murat leads the spectator to visit the odd universe of the parallel power settled in the slums of Maré. As the film director and screen play writer, she takes up her role of interpreter of one of the best known Shakespearean plays. In this sense, her intersemiotics translation of *Romeo and Juliet* can play a role of major importance, allowing for democratization and popularization of a Shakespearean text brought into contexts which are more familiar to the socially excluded spectator.

In the filmic translation, the brand of exclusion is inscribed in the separation of both worlds: the organized urban legal universe *versus* the transgressor and entropic universe of the slums. The ruptures generate astonishment on both parts, making translation between discourses nearly impossible. Fernanda, the ballet instructor, who comes from the legal world, believes it is possible to re-establish peace and dignity by means of dancing. But she is not able to reason with Dudu, her "protector," leader of the Blue faction, Jonathan's brother. Fernanda's involvement with the community is not seen with good eyes by her friend who's also a ballet dancer, a typical high-brow culture representative, and comes from the fancy neighbourhoods of Rio. "You have always had marginal taste," she tells Fernanda, who promptly responds: "*Good* marginal taste, by the way." Once more, the filmic text breaks with the aesthetics of the hegemonic centers who define the quality of an art work.

Analidia and Jonathan`s wedding is performed by Fernanda in a warehouse, where Carnival decorations and wagons are stored. There they pledge mutual love, before the eyes of their dance instructor, who blesses them just like the Shakespearean Friar Lawrence. On a pile of silver shredded paper—in a clear allusion to the star-crossed lovers—the couple makes love to the sound of Prokofiev's *Romeo and Juliet*.

The union of both lovers is translated by the *pas-de-deux* which they dance before the obliging eyes of the other members of the dance group and Fernanda. Their skills as dancers result in the possibility of a scholarship abroad which is promptly denied by Jonathan's brother Dudu. The young man is forbidden to leave the limits of Maré. In an intertext with *Hamlet*, the chorus of rappers announces: "Love puts us in weird situations. To face or not to face them is the question."

In order to make it possible for the young dancers and lovers the opportunity of personal development allowed by the new horizon, Fernanda simulates Jonathan's death. The idea is to have him escape in a coffin, but the young man in charge of alerting Analídia about the plan is intercepted by the opposite faction. The only information she gets comes through her girlfriends: Jonathan had been killed.

She immediately dashes off to see her husband's dead body, running desperately to the sound of Prokofiev's *Romeo and Juliet*. As she crosses a shooting field between the two factions, she is killed. Meanwhile, Dudu is told of his brother`s death and is taken by anger and wrath. Not knowing that his brother is alive in the coffin, Dudu shoots towards it. Also, to the sound of Prokofiev, the spectator sees then a thread of blood running through an invisible crack in the coffin.

From there, the camera moves through the unorganized architectural compound of the shanty town, where we see a waving flag of a popular soccer team. In voice-over the spectator is told: "The Community of Maré Radio Station now closes its daily activities." The image of a solitary rooster, who will probably announce brighter mornings, is also brought to the screen, associated to the voice-over.

And so ends this story of another Romeo and another Juliet, or Lucia Murat`s *Romeo and Juliet*. I have not attempted to build a critical study of the film. I have just argued that intersemiotic translation of canonical works of art, that is, "performances of mass media which remain excluded from the universities and museums, 'uncapable' of reading and looking at the high brow cultures because they ignore the history of knowledge and styles" (Canclini, 205) can help in the education of today's so-called plain individual. After all, as Silviano Santiago reminds us, in a peripheral country such as Brazil, it will not be through the painful exercise of a mere teaching of basic reading and writing skills that the excluded illiterate individual will assimilate information and use it in the understanding of society and the world where he/she lives. (Santiago, 129)

Translation reaches the public through the cinema, television, comic strips, cartoons, books not as another model, but as a producer of instability which speaks for itself, is unfaithful, and does not submit itself to the 'essence' of an origin. It sets its own logic. And through this very logic it offers a chance for democratization of the arts, bringing the outside world closer to the contemporary individual, in a country where a huge mass of culturally excluded people do not have access to the live performances or to texts published in a foreign language.

Works Cited

Canclini, Néstor Garcia. *Culturas Híbridas*. Trad. Heloísa Pezza Cintrao, Ana Regina Lessa. 4ª. ed. São Paulo: EDUNESP, 2008.

Deleuze, Gilles. Platão e o simulacro. In: *Lógica do Sentido*. Trad. Luiz Roberto Salinas Fortes. Sao Paulo: Perspectiva, 2006.

Heliodora, Barbara (trad.). *William Shakespeare: Tragédias e Comédias Sombrias*. Rio de Janeiro: Nova Aguilar, 2006.

Murat, Lucia. *Maré—Nossa História de Amor*. Genre: Musical. *Length:* 105 minutes. *Released in Brazil / France / Uruguay*, 2007.

Santiago, Silviano. *O Cosmopolitismo do Pobre: Crítica Literária e Crítica Cultural*. Belo Horizonte: Editora UFMG, 2004.

Stam, Robert. *Literature and Film: a guide to the theory and practice of film adaptation*. Oxford: Blackwell, 2005.

_____. *Literatura através do cinema: realismo, magia e a arte da adaptação*. Trad. Marie-Anne Kremer e Gláucia Renate Gonçalves. Belo Horizonte: Editora UFMG, 2008.

The Beauty, the Beast and the Sacred: Re-Reading Desdemona, Lavinia and Ophelia

CRISTIANE BUSATO SMITH
Arizona State University

Sacrifice—whether religious or secular—is central to the history of civilization and sacrificial patterns pervade tragedy, as classical studies on sacrifice and violence by Walter Burkert and René Girard demonstrate. The troubling phenomenon of the scapegoat, for instance, suggests that the death of the tragic hero brings redemption to the ills of a given society. Bearing the stains of his tragic flaw, the tragic hero will ultimately have to pay for it with his life. Nevertheless, we forgive the tragic hero because, as King Lear says, he is "more sinned against than sinning" (3.2.59). Yet, the tragic hero is not the focus of this paper, even though he harnesses most of the critical attention of the traditional scholarship devoted to tragedy, violence and sacrifice. I want, rather, to focus on the figure of the sacrificial heroine and explore her dramatic mechanism in relation to the sacred.

The liminal figure of the sacrificial heroine, of course, is hardly a Shakespearean invention, standing at the heart of Western civilization's sacrificial economy, but there is no doubt that Shakespeare paid special attention to the dramatic potential of female sacrifice by creating a memorable repertoire of heroines. My analysis of Lavinia, Ophelia and Desdemona as archetypal examples will link them to the sacred, a Janus-faced territory that places the Shakespearean heroines in an in-between, ambivalent status. As René Girard explains, the sacrificial heroine earns her sacrificial spurs "by reason of her weakness and relatively marginal social status. That is why she can be viewed as a quasi-sacred figure, both desired and disdained, alternatively elevated and abused." Girard's description resonates particularly well with Lavinia, Ophelia and Desdemona who will display the duality he refers to. In fact, the ambiguity related to the concept of the sacred can be established by retracing its etymology: it derives from the Latin term *sacer* which means both holy and accursed (Burkert 9). Frequently connected to the feminine, the sacred gives rise to the idea of difference and othering.

I will argue that Lavinia, Desdemona and Ophelia share a similar structural pattern and ritualistic tropes where the concept of the sacred finds particular use. Unjustly wronged, they undergo a radical process of moral and/or physical disfigurement which strips them of agency and inexorably leads them to their sacrificial deaths. That their passings can be read as part-compensatory and operate as atonement for a corrupt world they are entirely innocent of illustrates the mechanisms of the scapegoat (Girard 1972). In terms of animal imagery, Lavinia is compared to a doe (*Titus Andro*nicus 2.1.93) and a deer (3.1.91), Desdemona to an ewe (*Othello* 1.1.89)—animals whose religious and literary symbolisms connect them to the idea of victimization—while the "mermaid like" (*Hamlet* 4.7.187) Ophelia impersonates the sacrificial lamb in her watery death.

Indeed sheep, in the guise of the sacrificial lamb, figure notably in the Bible but were also regularly sacrificed in different cultures, especially in Greek and Latin ones, becoming the ultimate sacrificial animal. While the analysis of animal imagery has been dismissed by some as outdated, it was, nevertheless, through my research on the symbolisms of the deer that another intriguing intertextual possibility for Lavinia unfolds through the myth of Iphigenia and her sacrifice, one that, to my knowledge, has gone unnoticed by scholarship.

Desdemona [Singing]: The poor soul sat sighing by a sycamore
tree.
Sing all a green willow
Her hand on her bosom, her head on her knee

Sing willow, willow, willow.

With Desdemona, we encounter the tragic potentials of the self-sacrificial heroine. Her name is a derivation of the Greek *dusdaimon* which means unfortunate or ill-fated. Similar to Lavinia and Ophelia, Desdemona's tragic story underscores a radical transformation. At first, Desdemona seems to be courageous, confident, outspoken and strikingly bold. She runs away from her father's house to marry a Moorish soldier and boldly testifies before the Venetian Senate publicly declaring her love and asking permission to accompany her husband on his military mission in Cyprus. Described as a "warrior" by Othello, Desdemona is afraid of neither public speech nor of speaking her mind. She conspicuously clashes with the ideal image of the obedient silent wife which populated several early modern texts and, in a similar fashion to many unruly women in Shakespeare, pays a high penalty for her transgression. Chaste Desdemona is radically transfigured, in Othello's eyes, into "that cunning whore of Venice that married Othello" (4.2). In fact, in the sexually oppressive universe of *Othello*, Desdemona ironically metamorphoses into the profaned "white ewe" alluded to by Iago's sexual imagery that "an old black ram/ is tupping your white ewe" (1.1). Iago's initial intention was to pollute Brabantio's mind against Othello and indeed the image was so powerful that a spiteful Brabantio contaminates Othello as well by erroneously prophesying that "she [Desdemona] has deceived her father / and may thee" (1.2). In this sense, Desdemona's father's sense of betrayal is projected and introjected to her husband.

Desdemona's reaction to her husband's verbal and physical abuse is perplexity, silence, and an uncanny premonition of her untimely death. She patiently tolerates Othello's wrath, even when he strikes her in public. Her Christian virtues radiate throughout the play in words such as "sweet," "chaste," "heaven," "divine," "obedient," "heavenly true," and "angel." Indeed, Desdemona's treatment in *Othello*, polarizes her as saint or whore, both the problem and the solution—one of the indispensable characteristics of the sacrificial victim.

One of the rituals that prepare Desdemona for the sacrifice is the one that sees her singing the willow song (4.3). Not only does this scene suspend the crescendo of violence in the previous scenes but it also introduces an aesthetic hiatus in the play that displays Desdemona retreating briefly in the realm of music, memory and the sacred before she dies. The Willow Song ritualistically prepares the audience for the ultimate sacrifice Desdemona is about to submit to. Much as the mythical swan song, it shows Desdemona singing a song about an act of surrender and inevitability that is packed with pathos and melancholy, setting the right tone for the final scene.

The last ritual is Desdemona's death. In her deathbed, after being smothered by her husband, Desdemona hovers between life and death, and, in a play so concerned with honesty and lying it is interesting to note that the only "lie" the dying Desdemona tells is to exonerate Othello from his crime, which confirms and furthers her "sanctification."

Now reduced to the dead body of a beautiful woman, Desdemona's last rite is to die shrouded in her wedding sheets as she had eerily foreseen, immaculate, no blood stain to mar her fair skin, her body occupies centrestage. The ewe that had haunted her reputation abandons the profanity of Iago's discourse and Othello's pathological jealousy to represent Desdemona in its sacred form of the sacrificial lamb. Not only does the deathbed scene inscribe Desdemona as the quintessential symbol of female self-sacrifice but it also announces a dutiful return to the natural order of things—Othello kills himself and fulfills the function of the scapegoat. For Girard, this duality reflects "the metamorphosis the ritual victim is designed to effect: the victim draws to itself all the violence infecting the original victim and through its own death transforms this baneful violence into beneficial violence, into harmony and abundance."

Desdemona's body, however, in the sacred moment of her death, articulates the other side of the sacred becoming an example of *ars moriendi* in the Romantic trope of a "beautiful dead woman," a locus where the male gaze exercises its objectifying desires and fantasies, as Elizabeth Bronfen powerfully argues in *Over her Dead Body* (1992).

> Lavinia: She is a woman, therefore may be woo'd,
> She is a woman, therefore may be won,
> She is Lavinia, therefore must be lov'd. (*Titus Andronicus*)

Lavinia is the only beautiful daughter of the illustrious Roman general Titus Andronicus. Admired by her virtue and beauty, she is seen as virtuous, gracious, and is described by Bassianus as "Rome's rich ornament" (1.1.55). Indeed, in a warrior society like Rome, women were viewed as objects to be appropriated by force by the soldiers. Shakespeare draws on Roman history and literature to dramatize Lavinia's horror.

Lavinia's initial elevated status suffers a dramatic blow after the newly wed is violated and mutilated by Chiron and Demetrius. From then on, the disfigured Lavinia affords a uniquely unsettling bodily presence in *Titus Andronicus*: her hands and tongue severed to keep her silent, her body becomes a bleeding "map of woe" and a silent witness to the crime she suffered. As a general rule, mutilation involves martyrdom and, as Höfele explains, "the body is treated as parts: hands, ears, eyes, tongues, bones, throat, head entrails." Yet, can her severed members tell her whole story?

Associated with a doe in several moments of the play, Lavinia is cast in the role of prey when Demetrius announces his wish to rape her to his brother Chiron: "Chiron, we hunt not, we, with horse nor hound / But hope to pluck a dainty doe to the ground" (2.1.1). After the rape, Lavinia's uncle Marcus compares her to a stricken deer when he says he found her wandering around the forest "seeking to hide herself, as doth the deer / That hath receiv'd some unrecurring [incurable] wound" (3.1.4). Indeed, many writers have used the metaphor of the stalked, suffering and slaughtered deer to represent tormented characters. Deers, in particular, have been linked to sacrificial rituals and the motif of the sacrificial deer is also present in the myth of Iphigenia in a strikingly similar occurrence of sacrifice which doubles Lavinia's. One of the variations of the myth, *Iphigenia at Aulis* (written by Euripides in 410 BCE) has it that Iphigenia's father, King Agamemnon, couldn't bring his ships home because goddess Artemis cancelled the winds. Artemis declares she will only restore the winds if Agamemnon sacrifices Iphigenia. Agamemnon consents to Artemis and calls for Iphigenia to be brought to him on the pretext that she is to be married. Instead of the groom, the bride is met by her father on the altar and is penetrated through the throat by his sword. At the point the sword meets her throat, Iphigenia vanishes and the body of a deer appears in her place. Artemis sends back the winds and the Greeks achieve victory and fame.

As we can see, the structure of Iphigenia's sacrifice is similar to Lavinia's in many aspects. Both are guiltless of their fathers' crimes, both have the ritual of marriage broken. While Iphigenia is raped visually and metaphorically by her father through the sword, Lavinia suffers a second rape when she is asked to hold a staff in her wounded mouth and write the name of the crime and of the authors in the sand. Both as brides, Iphigenia and Lavinia are sacrificed by their fathers to atone for Greece or Rome. Both of them become the stricken deer, in a symbiotic relation that unites woman and animal through sacrifice. Whether Shakespeare read Euripides' *Iphigenia in*

Aulis or not is not as important here as it is to show that Iphigenia becomes one more victim in the signifying chain (Lavinia, Philomel (Ovid/Livy), Lucrece (Ovid/ Livy), Verginia (Livy).

Such *mys-en-abime* structure where one narrative points to the next also hints at the troubling fact that there is no exact point of departure for rape narratives, and maybe no end. In other words, Lavinia's plight has been told many times before and, as the intertextual chain suggests, will continue to be told. Shakespeare dramatizes this memorably. The motif of the deer— in the case of Iphigenia, helps to dislodge the sacrifice from her body and place it in the deer, while in Lavinia's case the focus is totally centered upon her mutilated body. With regards to the symbiosis of the deer with the woman where both become one for the sake of sacrifice, this has become a particularly well represented trope by female artists in different art forms and cultures. Cases in point are poet Emily Dickinson in "A Wounded Deer Leaps Highest" and Mexican painter Frida Kahlo in *El Venado Herido* (1946).

Lavinia's last sacrifice, similar to Ophelia's and Desdemona's, is self sacrificial and ritualistic: Lavinia is veiled representing both maid and bride but also hiding the stain of rape. According to Girard, the sacrificial victim has to be "expandable" for society and that is exactly what Lavinia has become for Rome. She can neither be daughter nor wife since she is no longer virtuous. She cannot bear children lest they carry her shame and dishonor. As Titus says: "Die, die, Lavinia, and thy shame with thee / And with thy shame thy father's sorrow die" (5.3.42-43). Thus, it is only through her death that Lavinia will be able to redeem the honor of her family and a new cycle can begin.

Ophelia: Clamb'ring to hang, an envious sliver broke, When down
her weedy trophies and herself fell in the weeping brook.
Her clothes spread wide and, mermaid-like, awhile they

> bore her up; which time she chanted snatches of old tunes, as one incapable of her own distress, or like a creature native and indued unto that element; (*Hamlet*)

Ophelia is one of the most intriguing self-sacrificial heroines in the Shakespearean canon. Initially an innocent girl, a dutiful daughter and sister and virginal lover, Ophelia undergoes a major transfiguration which leads her to madness and death.

Ophelia is used throughout the play—by Polonius, Laertes, Claudius, and is abused by Hamlet. At first, Polonius and Laertes reproach Ophelia for being naïve in her relation with Hamlet, claiming that "Hamlet is a prince out of thy star" (2.2). Underpinning her image as a chaste sex object, her father and brother lecture Ophelia on maintaining her virginity, lest she should let her "chaste treasure open/to his [Hamlet's] unmastered opportunity" (1.3). In addition, Ophelia will be used by Polonius and Claudius as a decoy to discover what ails Hamlet. Lastly, in the "nunnery scene," as if in validation of her status as object, Hamlet orders Ophelia to a nunnery: indirectly calling her a whore, since nunnery was a slang term for brothel in early modern England.

However, Ophelia's position as valued object of desire is underscored throughout the text in images such as the "the most beautified Ophelia," "fair Ophelia," the "beautiful Ophelia," the "nymph," "celestial," "rose," "mermaid-like." Confirming her significance as object of desire, we learn at her funeral, that Ophelia might have become Queen of Denmark, had events turned out differently.

With her father killed by Hamlet, her brother absent and Hamlet's brutal rejection, Ophelia feels the weight of the rottenness of the Danish court and becomes "a document of madness" (4.5), as her brother Laertes describes. Her madness is aestheticized by flowers and the songs she sings underscore the ritual nature of her disarray. Similar to Desdemona, Ophelia sings songs about lost love, lost chastity, and death.

Ophelia's status as sacrificial heroine is tied with her virginity as it was considered that the girl on the cusp of womanhood radiates a powerfully sacrificial aura. Many ancient societies regarded the virgin as marginal and expandable to the community. In ancient Greece, for instance, some parents would yield their daughters to save the city. Unmarried girls were also considered "untamed" so they were suitable to suffer the rites of death. Ophelia's virginity cannot be shared, lest she become "a breeder of sinners" (3.1.122), as Hamlet warns Polonius: "Let her not walk i'th' sun, Conception is a blessing" (2.2.184-5).

For several critics, however, Ophelia's sacrificial affinity has won her a place in the pantheon of Western legend. James Vest, for example, sees her in death as approaching the legendary apotheoses of myth (150-51). Ophelia's passing, like Jesus's, appears as a form of surrender rather than self-destruction (56). Indeed, her last words are unambiguously religious and sound like a benediction: "God a mercy on his soul / and of all Christian souls. God buy you."

This reading suggests that Ophelia's death can be seen as redemptive, functioning as atonement for the rottenness of Denmark; for it is only when Hamlet sees Ophelia in her coffin that he acts as "Hamlet the Dane," and will henceforth fulfil his task as a tragic hero, avenging his father's death and eventually accepting his own so as to restore order to the ailing state. The etymology of Ophelia's name—it derives from the Greek *opheleia*, meaning "help" or "succour"—confirms this redemptive mission. Ophelia thus becomes, in Girard's terms, a catalyst for "social metamorphosis." And Ophelia attains the status of an archetypal model as well as a cult heroine, one of Shakespeare's most textualized female characters.

Ophelia's connection with flowers and vegetation links her to a Flora figure, but in her association with a mermaid she becomes one with the water, her "own element." In her metamorphosis as mermaid, she becomes a "fish-woman," an acquatic creature belonging to the mythical sphere. While the symbolism of the mermaid as temptress, translates Ophelia's dual treatment in *Hamlet*, the fish, being the oldest Christian symbol of Christ, bears rich religious significance. Cirlot notes that the fish is also symbolic of sacrifice and others associate it with baptism. Indeed Ophelia's watery death can be seen to operate as a baptism. Singing old lauds and wearing her "weedy coronet," which suggests a crown of thorns, Ophelia surrenders to her watery death, suggesting redemption and purification.

In this essay, I have attempted to approach the intersections of the woman, the beast and the sacred through the female body, death and sacrifice. The sacred is not synonymous with the divine, but according to Kristeva, women have a particular affinity with it through both the psychic freight of becoming mothers and the disposition of the feminine in a patriarchal society which places women as a figure of disillusion. Indeed, the feminine and the sacred seem to have a long standing relationship that is undeniably alive in our society in the guise of eating disorders, rampant plastic surgery and the glamourization of the violence against the feminine body in movies and the fashion industry.

Such objectification of the female body beastializes women and renders the association of women and animal a frequent trope. The ewe, the deer and the fish-woman/mermaid provide a crucial element in my reading of Desdemona, Lavinia and Ophelia. They bring into view the close relationship between woman and animal in patriarchal thought. Indeed, as Hélène Cixous and Catherine Clément argue in *The Newly-Born Woman* (1975), patriarchy has been organized in a system of binarisms which places women firmly on the side of "nature," while "culture" is the province of men. By virtue of men's intellectual "superiority," men must domesticate women's irrational or "animalesque" side in a similar way that animals need to be domesticated. Images of the "man-hunter" and the "hunted woman" which Lavinia memorably incorporates, as well the lascivious "white ewe" which takes possession of Othello's mind, and the mystical mermaid that Ophelia embodies in her poeticized watery death, are paradigmatic examples of this tendency. The fact that these animals/being can also incorporate aspects of sacrifice that bring to the fore the ambiguity of the sacred supports my main arguments.

"The death of a beautiful woman" wrote Edgar Allan Poe, is "the most poetical topic in the world." For all Poe's sexism, the concept of aestheticized death is unmistakably gendered, and has been all-encompassing in Western culture from the earliest times. Beauty and death, down through the ages, have been linked with the universal figure of Woman. The circulation of beautiful dead women in art, images of Ophelia being a thriving example, is so visible that it has become invisible. Indeed, if we consider death as a sacred moment, here lies an important aspect of the Janus-faced nature of the sacred, its undecidability, as sacred and cursed, present in the Latin term *sacer*.

It is in the very otherness of their tragedies that Lavinia, Ophelia and Desdemona articulate the complex aspects of sacrifice and the sacred. Tragedies that are not forged in the great deeds and downfall of the tragic hero but rather in the breaches of their wounds, sacrifices, silences, and deaths.

Shakespeare and the Culture of Innovation

C.N. AJIT
Society for Innovation and Development
Indian Institute of Science, Bangalore

"There is nothing good or bad but thinking makes it so"

Hamlet

Culture of Innovation has been as basic to humanity as the culture of survival. There has been continuous effort by the human race to innovate so as to make this world a better place to live in. Contemporary Definition of Innovation reads as "Exploitation of a new idea for a wide range of applications and commercialization." Since by the very definition, Innovation has Material reward as its goal, the pursuit has been competitive resulting in application of strategies available at that point of time for winning. Innovation is basically of two kinds, viz. Sustaining and Disruptive. While the former caters to the felt needs of the society at that point of time, the latter caters to supposedly unfelt and future needs.

In this paper we examine the mechanisms which over a long period of time have been utilized to motivate, execute and successfully monetize the two kinds of innovation. In the process we examine the art of converting 'unfelt' into 'felt' and the perspectives of 'Past influencing the Present' and of 'Truth following Fiction'. This exercise will mainly be based on examples drawn from the works of the Bard.

There have been frequent discussions in Culture Study groups on how the term 'culture' is being used in increasingly restrictive sense with passing of time. To give some examples, 'pub culture' or 'techie culture' are popular terminology. It would be very interesting to take a journey back in time and find that the use of the term 'culture' takes on an increasingly broader perspective. In this journey when we reach possibly the very beginning, we find that there has been only one connotation for 'culture' and that was the 'culture of survival'. This Culture supposedly originated to protect humanity from the vagaries of nature and possibly that is how frequently we find that Culture has been in opposition with Nature. With the urge of humanity to attempt to make this world a better place to live in, possibly another facet of culture which may be as old as the 'Culture of Survival' is the 'Culture of Innovation' . In this context it would be very relevant to discuss 'culture of innovation' in relation to Shakespeare who is as much for all ages as culture.

In this paper, we look at two aspects of the relation between the Bard and the culture of innovation. The first is as to how he upheld the value system of the culture of innovation. In the second part, we look at some of the innovative aspects in his works.

Traditionally, culture has been described through the onion peel model with 'Rituals' being the outermost and 'Symbols' , 'Heroes' and 'Values' being the progressive inner layers as we move towards the core. The model recognizes 'Values' as being the core of culture. Now, we look at such value system in the case of 'Culture of Innovation' which is the subject of discussion in this paper.

To be able to innovate, a person has to have the quality of humility inculcated firmly. One famous example of the illustration of this quality is the paradoxical saying by Socrates: "I only know that I know nothing." To illustrate a couple of examples from Shakespeare's *Hamlet* reflecting this value:

> There are more things in heaven and earth, Horatio, than are dreamt of in your philosophy.
>
> We know what we are, but know not what we may be.

Another value as important as humility to the Innovative mindset is belief in the supremacy of truth. Isaac Newton once had this to say about his belief in truth "Pluto is my friend—Aristotle is my friend—Truth is a greater friend." Shakespeare has highlighted this value often in his works and some good examples are:

> Truth is Truth to the end of reckoning (*Measure for Measure*)
>
> This above all: to thine self be true (*Hamlet*)

The ability to continue one's work even if one were to appear to be foolish to the rest of the world is one of the major strengths needed for innovation. It was Charles Darwin who once said: "I love fools' experiments. I am always making them." Perhaps it is in reflecting on this aspect of life that Shakespeare has been at his literary best. The way he has illustrated the underlying wisdom beneath what is seemingly foolish has already been the centre of many studies of his works. Here, we just take a look at some of those gems:

> The wise man knows himself to be a fool. (*Measure for Measure*)
>
> This great stage of fools. (*As You Like It*)

The innovator while being aware of the investment and involvement in his pursuits has to be immune to the mistakes which may be part of the pursuit. This inevitability has been nicely expressed by Albert Einstein thus, "A person who never made a mistake, never tried anything new." A similar sentiment has been reinforced by Shakespeare at many places in different contexts.

> Our doubts are traitors and make us lose the good we oft might win by fearing to attempt (Measure for Measure)
>
> Make not your thoughts your prisons (Anthony and Cleopatra)

At the outset, Shakespeare can possibly be called the Greatest Innovator in literature for the way he picked up existing plots in most cases and added value through literary imagination to come up with products that would sell for all times to come. Bill Bryson attributes this to the high level of Assimilative Intelligence Shakespeare possessed. Whether the reward perception in the mind of the Bard was Intellectual or Material, is a question that may not have a definite answer, but facts show that both the reward perceptions have largely been met over time and the product still sells. A quick look at couple of innovative ideas from the works with reference to the contemporary scenario.

(a) Whenever there is an innovation, to monetize the effort, the innovator tries best to project a felt need of the society for that product though there may not be one. A case in point where an attempt for converting unfelt into felt need in today's world is the marketing of Fairness cream for men. Shakespeare has a nice lesson to offer on this, in the way Iago plays on Othello's mind to make him colour conscious.

(b) While the Bard says "Past is Prologue," the way he creates a situation where truth follows fiction through the prophecies of the witches in *Macbeth*. This again is a lesson in disruptive innovation used very convincingly. While the literary perspective on the prophecies has been studied extensively, the concept is very much in practice today with Modern medical specialists playing the witches with their prophecies on their Patients.

(c) Selling dreams imaginatively is another innovative concept which Shakespeare has very successfully demonstrated in his works like *Romeo and Juliet*. The same has undergone sustaining innovation over time in the film industry and continues to bring in big money for the practitioners.

(d) While humanity celebrated the application of Information and Communication Technologies during the second half of the twentieth century, the research efforts of this century seem to be mainly directed towards Cognition and Consciousness. The Information overload and rapid discontinuities in life have given rise to an increasing need to adapt to another kind of consciousness. While the ancient scripts like the *Gita* are being revisited for useful inputs in this effort, the works of the Bard can also definitely help humanity adapt to the future

The author sincerely hopes to have thrown some light on the role of Shakespeare on the culture of innovation both as a Guru of the value system and as an astute participant of that culture. This study is by no way complete but hopes to trigger further Inter- and Trans-disciplinary studies.

Shakespearean *Mahabharata*: *A Midsummer Night's Dream* as *Pramilarjuniyam* in Kannada

SAKSHI SONI AND T.S. SATYANATH
University of Delhi

Early Shakespearian translations, generally called 'adaptations', deviate significantly from their 'originals' and have often been labelled, criticized and even rejected as 'infidel' within the frame of Eurocentric theory of translation. While the conceptual category of 'tellings' may prompt us to accept such deviations in Shakespearian adaptations, the very fact that they were done for theatre and that the nineteenth century audience sensibilities demanded such deviations need to be problematized in order to understand their cultural significance. Furthermore, Indian folk theatre was essentially oral in nature and provided several components to the newly emerging proscenium theatre. These aspects direct us to look for cultural explanations rather than taking a text-centered approach and thereby categorizing adaptations in general as 'infidel'. It has been suggested here that the early theatrical adaptations of Shakespeare need to be understood as attempts of cultural mappings rather than as transfer of colonial knowledge.

Within the background of theoretical issues raised above, this paper attempts to map how a Kannada adaptation of Shakespeare's play *A Midsummer Night's Dream* (1595) by Srikantheshgowda in 1896 as *Pramilarjuniyam*, gets mapped into the structure of one of the episodes of the *Mahabharata*. Whereas the Athenians' episode of Theseus and Hippolyta corresponds to the Arjuna and Pramila episode of the *Jaiminiya*

Mahabharata, the Fairies' episode of Oberon and Titania corresponds to the episode of Manmatha and Rati and the Mechanicals acting troupe's performance corresponds to the performance of *Samadhi Parinaya* (literally, 'Marriage in the grave'). There are several instances in Medieval Indian vernacular tellings and renderings, in which the cosmopolitan Sanskritic narratives undergo a process of re-mythicization as can be noticed in the case of *Pramilarjuniyam*. Furthermore, the performance of Pyramus and Thisbe becomes Ramavarma-Lilavati in *Pramilarjuniyam*, linking it to the Kannada adaptation of *Romeo and Juliet* as *Ramavarma Lilavati Caritre* (1889) translated by Anandarao. The enactment of Samadhi Parinaya in *Pramilarjuniyam* actually refers to an abridged version of *Ramavarma Lilavati Caritre*.

Mapping the cultural isoglosses in which the early Kannada translations/ adaptations were undertaken on the one hand and the audience sensibilities on the other, this paper attempts to shift the focus of translation studies to the margins, thereby methodologically pleading for a margino-centric approach instead of a Eurocentric approach. The paper consists of four parts. The first part consists of introductory remarks and proposes a theoretical model for understanding the hybridity between colonial modernity and Indian traditionality/ classicism. In the second part, a comparative perspective of the two texts has been outlined. The third part problematizes the nineteenth century theatre as public sphere and early translations in terms of their structural characteristics. The last part discusses the implications of hybridity in theatre and pleads for a study of early adaptations at multiple levels, making use of a comparative perspective, incorporation of transmedial representations and locating them within the overlapping zone of a composite culture that involves colonial modernity, nationalism and regional identity formations.

The term 'Shakespearean *Mahabharata*' actually subsumes a hybrid category. It suggests an interface zone of colonial modernity and Indian traditionality/classicism, in which the European and the Indian categories are blended to create a new variety. While the European modernity was a reaction to realism, the Indian modernity was actually contesting traditionality. Within the pro-modernity and pro-traditionality debates of early Indian modernism, a third hybrid position appears to have gained prominence. No other schematic representation than the sketch given in Figure 1 could rightly capture the complexity of hybridity suggested here. Adya Rangacharya's (Sriranga) article 'Samanyara Shakespeare' (meaning, 'Shakespeare of ordinary people') in *Shakespiyarige namaskara* (meaning, 'saluting Shakespeare'), edited by Balurao (1966), consists of an illustrative sketch by the artist R.S. Naidu, a renowned painter and faculty at the Jaganmohana School of Arts, Mysore to demonstrate "Kalidasa as Shakespeare of Hindustan." A close reading of the following sketch helps us to appreciate its significance. Satyanath's (2004: 71) reading of the sketch is as follows: 'Kalidasa and Shakespeare are represented with hand in hand and dressed in appropriate attires, suitable to the worlds that they represent. While Kalidasa has a palm-leaf manuscript in his hand, Shakespeare has a scroll. Everything looks like a perfect demonstration of a harmonious East-West encounter. However, a closer look reveals that Kalidasa is represented on the right side and Shakespeare to his left. We all know that in Indian iconographic tradition, *vāma* (left) conventionally suggests inferiority and insignificance with reference to its right counterpart.'

Here, Kalidasa could be easily replaced by Vyasa or any other ancient Indian bard and this provides the appropriate entry point for this paper. The sketch of Naidu could as well serve as an ideal model of hybridity between colonial modernity and Indian traditionality/classicism that the nineteenth century Indian scholarship has constructed. At the same time, it could also serve a margino-centric approach i.e. reading hybridity in terms of Indian conventions or understanding Shakespeare through Kalidasa. It is not just a coincidence that during the period of early Indian modernity several translators of Kalidasa in Indian languages were also translating Shakespeare.

Figure 1: Sketch by R.S. Naidu suggesting hybridity of modernity and traditionality/classicism

The early adaptations of Shakespeare into Indian languages, many of which have often been claimed as infidel and looked down, actually deserve a relook as zones of hybridity constructed from a margino-centric point of view. If these adaptations could be viewed as a negotiation between the European and Indian cultural systems, then we can have at least two positions of viewing the process of translation. The first one is a monogenetic Euro-centric position of mapping the correspondences between the original and the translated texts. This could be roughly designated as influence and reception model. Alternatively, we can think of an India-centric model, pluralistic in nature, from which the translation process could be mapped. This maps the translation process from diametrically opposite and multiple positions which provide an opportunity to understand adaptations within the cultural context in which they were produced and consumed. Such a position also reverses the dominant Euro-centric view of translation theory and instead provides margino-centric views from the peripheries in the form of an array of pluralistic perspectives of the translating cultures. Thus, the issue of originality and infidelity in translation is contested and in turn how a recipient culture maps and negotiates the cultural differences is addressed. In fact, many early translators have pointed out that it is the cultural mismatch that prompted them to adapt rather than seek for literal translation. Within this background, this paper intends to take up the processes involved in the adaptation of Shakespeare's *A Midsummer Night's Dream* as *Pramilarjuniyam* in Kannada.

Although the adaptations of Shakespeare start as early as 1871 in Kannada, it is only after the Parsi theatre visited the princely court of Mysore in 1880, that the theatre and translation activity in the region started vigorously. As a matter of fact, at least four translations of *A Midsummer Night's Dream* have been reported in Kannada, namely K. Vasudevacharya's *Vasantayamini Swapnacamatkara Natakavu* (1890), Srikantheshgowda's *Pramilarjuniyam* (1896), V. Huyilagola's *Nadubesageya Iruluganasu* (1963) and Nisar Ahmad's *A Midsummer Night's Dream* (1974).

It is possible that the cue for Srikantheshgowda's adaptation might as well have come from Shakespearean plot itself as there are at least two Indian connections within the play. However, Vasudevacharya's title, which roughly translates as 'spring-night's dream-magic play', doesn't seem to suggest the *Mahabharata* equation that Srikantheshgowda is trying to forge. The first Indian connection refers to the woods wherein there are two very different groups of characters, of which the first is a band of fairies, including Oberon, the fairy king, and Titania, his queen, who have recently returned from India to bless the marriage of Theseus and Hippolyta. The second Indian connection is that of Oberon and Titania who are at odds over an orphan young Indian prince (*gandharva balaka* in *Pramilarjuniyam*) given to Titania by the prince's mother; the boy is so beautiful that Oberon wishes to make him a knight or henchman, which Titania refuses. Oberon is jealous of the child as Titania lavishes all care on him, neglecting Oberon. In *Pramilarjuniyam*, Manmatha wants to have him as one of his five arrows (*pancha shara*).

To put it briefly, table 1 lists Shakespearean characters and their corresponding transformations in *Pramilarjuniyam* done in terms of Indian mythology, the epic *Mahabharata* and the caste system. The world of fairies gets mapped into the world of Rati and Manmatha of the Hindu pantheon, the Athenian world corresponds to the Pramila and Arjuna episode of the *Jaiminya Mahabharata*, and the Mechanicals in accordance with the artisan and servicing castes within the Indian caste system.

In the play *Pramilarjuniyam*, the playwright using the conventions of a Sanskrit play makes the Sutradhara and Nati initiate and introduce the play in the form of a *Nandi* (prelude of the play) which has also been called 'Prastavna' (introduction). Father Friar or Pujyapada Yogeshwara who solemnizes the marriage between Romeo and Juliet is Nenebarada Nagappa (the one who shouldn't be remembered), the barber, belonging to the untouchable caste. He also has a disciple performed by Darji Santuram Vithoba (a tailor by profession). Another interesting feature of the adaptation is that the play within the play 'Pyramus and Thisbe' gets transformed into the Kannada version of *Romeo and Juliet* titled as *Ramaverma Lilavati Charitre*, translated by Anandrao (1889). More remarkable is the fact that this version of the otherwise tragic play *Romeo and Juliet* ends as a comedy, wherein Pujyapada Yogeshwara, Friar Lawrence prays to Lord Vishnu, who in turn appears on the stage, and brings Romeo and Juliet back to life (Satyanath, 2004).

Table 1: Table showing the correspondences between Shakespearean characters in *A Midsummer Night's Dream* and Srikantheshgowda's *Pramilarjuniyam*

Shakespearean characters	**Transformed Characters in the adaptation**
The Fairies	
Oberon, the fairy king	Manmatha, God of love
Titania, the fairy queen and wife of Oberon	Rati Devi, wife of Manmatha
Puck/ Robin Goodfellow, servant to Oberon	Ashuga, the charioteer of Manmatha
Titania's fairy servants namely Peaseblossom, Cobweb, Moth, Mustardseed and others	Sakhis of Rati Devi—Malati, Madhavi, Mallika, Manjari and a Kechari (one who can fly)
The Athenians	
Theseus, duke of Athens	Arjuna in the Malabar region, Malayala
Hippolyta, queen of the Amazons, betrothed to Theseus	Pramila, queen of the Malayala
Philostrate, Master of the revels	Not represented
Egeus, father of Hermia, wants her to marry Demetrius	Menava, a Malayalee, father of Kairave, wants her to marry Vasanta
Hermia, in love with Lysander	Kairave, in love with Jayanta
Helena, in love with Demetrius	Padmini, in love with Vasanta
Lysander, in love with Hermia	Jayanta, in love with Kairave
Demetrius, in love with Hermia at first but later loves and	Vasanta, in love with Kairave at first but later loves and

marries Helena	marries Padmini
The Mechanicals (acting troupe)	
Peter Quince, carpenter, leads the troupe and plays Prologue	Vajara Mayachari, a carpenter, performs Sutradhara
Nick Bottom, weaver, plays Pyramus	Madivala Machaiya, washerman, plays Romeo
Francis Flute, bellows mender, plays Thisbe	Kulalakuntashetty, a potter, plays Juliet
Robin Starveling, tailor, plays Moonshine	Kammara Kadaiya, a blacksmith, plays Moon
Tom Snout, tinker, plays wall	Not named
Snug, joiner, plays lion	Not represented

Apart from this, there is also an interesting intertextuality with Kalidasa's *Shakuntalam* in *Pramilarjuniyam*. It has already been mentioned that many of the translators who translated Shakespeare have also translated Kalidasa during the early phase of modern Indian theatre. This intertextuality appears in the exchanges between Arjuna and Parmila [Act (*anka*) I scene 1 (*sthana*)]. Arjuna proposes to Pramila for a *'gandharva vivaha'* and she responds to it. "Priya, what is famous in the *puranas* is not just the *gandharva vivaha*; equally famous is the fact that because of *gandharva vivaha* several women (*kaminis*) have been cheated by men's inconstancy (*purusha chapalya*).

Arjuna's reply to this directly refers to the play Kalidasa's *Abhijnana Shakuntalam*: "Oh, I understand your hesitation; That Dushyanta, after having fulfilled his desires, told Shakuntala who had come to meet him, that he could not remember having seen her and thus deceived (*mosa*) her. How *gandharva vivaha* itself could be considered as deceiving? Why are you imposing his character on every one?"

There is also an instance of intertextuality with the story of *Mahabharata.* In the course of the conversation between Arjuna and Pramila, the reference to Draupadi and her polyandrous marriage with five Pandavas and even Arjuna's marriage with Chitrangada, princess of Manipur comes under their discussion. Thus, the entire *Mahabharata* is brought into the frame in this scene. It is needless to mention here that *Shakuntalopakhyana* itself is an integral part of the *Mahabharata.*

One also notices intertextuality with one of the Kannada translations of the Shakespearean play, *Romeo and Juliet.* The play within the play 'Samadhi Parinaya' in *Pramilarjuniyam* (corresponding to the episode of 'Pyramus and Thisbe' in *A Midsummer Night's Dream*) actually refers to *Ramavarma Lilavati Charitre* by Ananda Rao (1889), a translation of *Romeo and Juliet.* In addition, there is also a reference in the bibliographies to another version which has been translated by Srikantheshagowda himself from *Romeo and Juliet* with the same title *Ramavarma Lilavati Charitre1.* Thus, *Pramilarjuniyam* constructs a dense intertextuality with classical Indian literary culture on the one hand and contemporary literary cultures on the other hand. Furthermore, attempts have been made to incorporate colonial modernity through Shakespeare and nationalist dimensions through incorporation of pan-Indian conventions. Not only *Nandi*, and the characters of Sutradhara and Nati have been introduced but also metrical and musical conventions that are characteristic to translations of Sanskrit plays into Kannada have been incorporated into *Pramilarjuniyam.* As a matter of fact, it is here that we need to consider the nineteenth century modern Indian theatre in general and Kannada theatre in particular as a public sphere within the context of a hybridity comprising classicism, colonial modernity, nationalistic tendencies and the Kannada linguistic identity formation processes.

There is a need to look at early modern translations and adaptations for the new proscenium theatre from an audience and culture-centred perspective in order to capture and understand the transformations. Let us see how the Kannada translation of Kalidasa's *Shakuntalam* by Curamari Sheshagirirao (1869) and Srikantheshagowda's *Pramilarjuniyam* are structured and the significant role played by the cultural sensibilities of the audience in the formulation of these translations. The verse format of Kalidasa has been translated into the corresponding verse format in Kannada, sometimes retaining the same metre while at other times experimenting with a different one but from the Sanskrit metrical system (*vritta* and *kanda*). Srikantheshagowda uses the same metrical system in his adaptation.

The prosaic Sanskrit dialogues of Kalidasa have been translated by Sheshgirirao into a colloquial variety of speech from the North Karnataka region. However, Srikantheshagowda uses the standard literary (*granthika*) variety of Mysore Kannada for higher-level characters (the *Mahabharata* and *Rati-Manmatha* episodes) and a lower colloquial variety (*gramya*, rural) for the mechanicals (play within a play). Several songs have been written by both the translators to suit the nature of the musical theatre that was prevalent and popular around that time in Marathi *Sangeet natak*, Parsi theatre and Kannada folk theatre, which were new introductions into these translations. The songs have been claimed to be highly lyrical and poetic by the critics. Although the Sanskrit metrical system is sung melodiously in the *gamaka/alap* style to the classical tunes (Hindustani and Karnataki), the songs are based on popular tunes from the classical music (Hindustani and Karnataki).

The songs for the lower class characters either adopt folk tunes (c.f. *lavani*) or classical ragas sung in the folk style. Many of them appear to have remained popular, sometimes, even spilling into the domestic world. The ornamentation of language representing a high level ornamentation in *kandas* and *vrattas*, along with the use of classical music catered to the sophisticated taste of the elite section of the audience. A high degree of lyrical poetry in songs and its popular singing style catered to the sensibilities of the newly emerging middle class. The prosaic dialogues (both the standard and rural varieties), the bawdy jokes and the folk tunes catered to the taste of the ordinary people. Thus, the textual structure and the musical structure of these plays, be they adaptations of Kalidasa (classical) or Shakespeare (modern) addressed a hybrid and composite audience structure of the nineteenth century public sphere.

Whereas the translation of *Shakuntalam* contains classical *ragas* from Karnataki and Hindustani styles and also folk tunes, *Pramilarjuniyam* has more or less a similar format, though Karnataki ragas are more frequently used (popular Telugu and Kannada tunes). It is interesting to point out that both translations/adaptations consistently use a *gamaka/alap* style for verse (slow style of singing without instruments), *raga*s for songs (music with *tabala/mridangam/dholak*) and the folk tunes for popular numbers.

There is a need to understand these components of translation from the point of view of audience sensibility in public sphere. The early modern theatre was itinerary in nature and professional in approach. Hence, its audience was not only diverse but also had diverse regional sensibilities. This suggests that not only was the audience sensibility differentiated vertically (elite, middle class and lower) but also as a much more complex level horizontally (spatially or regionally or even linguistically). We want to suggest that this component of diversity has gone into the construction of these adaptations. The use of Sanskrit verse format and the *gamaka/alap* style of music suggest that attempts were made to preserve the classical dimension of Sanskrit/Kannada literary tradition (ornamentation in text and music) within the adaptations. This was done to cater to the needs of the elite community of the audience. We need to remember that these verses could only be recited melodiously in *gamaka/alap* style. In addition, it gave the actor enough liberty to explore both the lyrical and musical dimensions of the metrical verse.

However, a majority of the audience was probably the ordinary masses. Verse format was too pedantic a style for them. Hence, the dialogues were written in standard and local varieties (sometimes even bilingual). The songs making use of the classical *raga*s, were a characteristic of the folk theatre, though diluted in their classicism. However, they have been conditioned by the rhythmic beat of *tabla*, the refrain-verse combination and a pre-mediated trajectory. These songs used to follow the tunes of classical style of music, both Hindustani and Karnataki. The songs bridged the gap that existed between classical verse format and the standard/vulgar dialect format of the dialogues and created a smooth intermediate zone. They also catered to the sensibilities of a newly emerging middle class who were familiar with the English musicals and the Parsi theatre. Interestingly, this song format appears to be in continuity with the repertoire of medieval Bhakti sectarian communities, in which the musical and lyrical aspects are extensively interwoven. In fact, both Sheshagirirao and Srikantheshagowda systematically mention the tunes to be used for the songs. Whereas *Shakuntalam*'s songs use tunes of famous Hindustani, Karnataki, devotional (bhakti) and folk tunes, *Pramilarjuniyam* songs are based on Telugu devotional tunes. The very fact that the two texts were written and used in the northern and southern parts of Karnataka explains the sensitivity of the translators to their audience community.

The discussion on the structuring of the translation process vis-à-vis the nineteenth century theatrical public sphere can be shown as follows. These adaptations were actually catering to three levels of audience, the elite, the newly emerging middle class and the folk, and made use of appropriate styles of metrical format, music format and language varieties. The entire discussion could be diagrammatically represented as shown in figure 2.

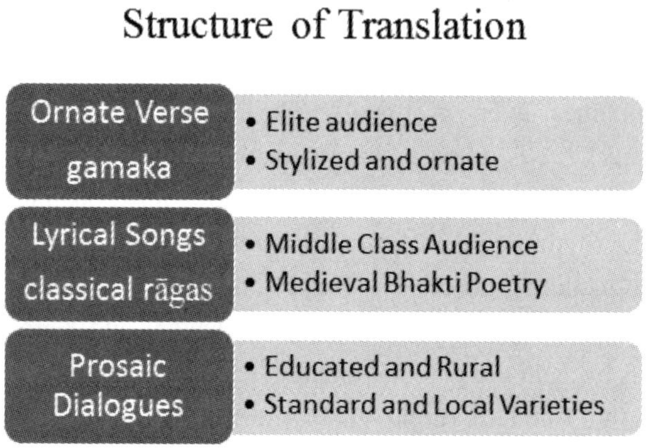

Figure 2. Diagram showing the hybridity of the nineteenth century theatrical public sphere

The *Mahabharata* theme in *Pramilarjuniyam* incorporates the hybridity at several levels. However, it needs to be underscored that such a hybridity is constructed from the cultural point of view of the translating community, a margino-centric view and not the other way. Meticulously choosing the trope of a pan-Indian epic theme such as the *Mahabharata* for the adaptation of a Shakespearean plot, may as well be understood as a nation-building process. As pointed out previously in the paper, at all the three levels—the textual format (*vrtta*, song, dialogue), musical format (*gamaka/alap*, popular and folk) and linguistic format (standard and dialect/local)—we can see the adaptation systematically attempting to cater to the needs of a newly emerging diverse/hybrid cultural community. In turning *A*

Midsummer Night's Dream into *Pramilarjuniyam*, Srikantheshgowda also transforms the Royal Athenian world into the earthly world of the *Mahabharata* (*Jaminiya Bharata*, also ascribed to Vyasa), the Fairy world into the Heavenly world of Rati and Manmatha and the World of the Mechanicals into an Indian caste-graded artisan community. Thus, the three-level adaptation strategy used is not just accidental but a carefully crafted adaptation to suit the newly emerging social epistemology and aesthetic conventions of the mid-nineteenth century Karnataka region. There are enough possibilities for extending this generalization to a pan-Indian level as a model of translation strategy that emerged during the late nineteenth century.

Shifting the focus from a Euro-centric language-centered reading of cultural transactions like translation, the reading of *Pramilarjuniyam* attempted here shifts the focus to the cultural context of the translating language, thereby pleading for a margino-centric approach for the study of translations. Furthermore, 'Shakespearian Mahabharata' as a conceptual category not only helps us to understand and appreciate the strategies and processes of early Indian theatre but also the techniques and models used by translators during the phase of early Indian translations/adaptations. All these points call for a review of early adaptations at multiple levels, making use of comparative Indian perspective, incorporation of transmedial representations and the intersecting zone of composite culture involving colonial modernity, nationalism and regional identity formation.

Shakespeare's *Romeo and Juliet*: A Study in the Light of Sufism

ABHAY LEONARD EKKA
D.A.V.P.G. College, Varanasi

> But now faith, hope, love abide these three; but the greatest of these is love. (St. Paul *I Corinthians* 13:13)

Shakespeare's greatness, one critic said, lay in his "comprehensive soul." That is the most poetic summation of a dramatic genius that has never been equalled. But if Shakespeare's plays and sonnets are the monuments of a remarkable genius, they are also the monuments of a remarkable posterity of human wisdom and medieval tradition of moral teachings through allegories. The heightened imitation of Nature in poetry inspires humans to virtuousness and civility, and ultimately to the uprightness of the human mind. The same finds expression in Shakespeare's plays. The underlying theme of a great part of Elizabethan literature is a constant conflict between individualism and the preconceived sense of moral order. Literary playwrights borrowed freely from popular sources, sermons, street ballads and their like.

No dramatist can create live characters save by bequeathing the best of oneself into one's work of art, scattering among them a largess of one's own qualities, wit, comprehensive cogent philosophy, rhythm of action and simplicity or complexity of one's own nature. Shakespeare excelled in all of them, all the time, or at least majority of times, as he teased and tormented them with his deep insight into human psyche on another. Plays like those of Shakespeare are written in blood; (as Hopkins says about his 'Terrible Sonnets') not run cold, but running warm and lively through the author's veins and spill like molten lava on every word that he writes. Renaissance resulted in a desire for a more productive form of scientific learning. Shakespearean plays depict the yearning for scientific learning and human philosophy in its more myriad and intense form. It is his unquestioned genius that made him so appealing to the era of flux in which he wrote and make him relevant even today after so much scientific advancement. It is widely accepted that Shakespeare's supreme gift is his universality. He was not of an age but for all times because his characters are true to the eternal aspects of human life and not limited to any contemporary society. Shakespeare saw and understood too much, could pierce the heart with too many passions, could realize the actual play of life, without falling in bondage to any power.

In the play *Romeo and Juliet*, Shakespeare depicts some of the aspects of human emotions and passions like: love-hatred, patience-impatience, forgiveness-vengeance etc. but here in the paper I shall analyze and concentrate on the nature of love and human relationships depicted in the play. Sufism is a branch in the world of philosophies. In *Romeo and Juliet* the hero and heroine represent or become true Sufis. In Sufism truth is considered as the ultimate reality of life. The practice of Sufism is the intention to go towards the truth, by means of love and devotion. Love and devotion are the spiritual path or way towards God. In the play, the lovers, Romeo and Juliet are united by the means and power of love. Thus, they become Sufis and attain their goal of life.

In Act II scene II of the play Juliet expresses her love for Romeo:

> My bounty is as boundless as the sea, my love as deep.
> The more I give to thee, the more I have, for both are infinite.[1]

The heartfelt love of Romeo for Juliet is exquisitely expressed in the answer of Romeo when Juliet asks him how and why he has risked his life by climbing over the boundary wall of the Capulates:

> With love's light wings did I o'erperch these walls,
> For stony limits cannot hold love out.
> And what love can do, that dares love attempt.
> Therefore thy kinsmen are no stop to me. (Act II Scene II)

For the sake of love Romeo is ready to change his name or to be baptized:

> I take thee at thy word. Call me but love, and I'll be new baptized.
> Henceforth I never will be Romeo.

Further he says:

> My name, dear saint, is hateful to myself,
> Because it is an enemy to thee.
> Had I written, I would tear the word.

In the following lines Romeo is cherishing and relishing the sweetness of love:

> It is my soul that calls upon my name.
> How silver-sweet sound lovers' tongues by night,
> Like softest music to attending ears.

Likewise Juliet is also eager to know about the opinion of Romeo of their marriage, so she inquires from her nurse:

> I'faith, I am sorry that thou art not well.
> Sweet, sweet, sweet Nurse, tell me what says my love?
> (Act II Scene V)

When Romeo is banished Juliet thinks that their love is forsaken. Thus she is ready to embrace death; at that moment the Nurse tells that Romeo will be here at night, Juliet boldly confesses her love for Romeo:

> O, find him! give this ring to my true knight

And bid him come to take his last farewell. (Act III Scene II)

We see that Juliet is in desperate love that she is even ready to sacrifice her life for the sake of love—live by love or die for love:

If all else fail, myself have power to die.
Do thou but call my resolution wise,
And with this knife I'll help it presently.
Be not so long to speak: I long to die
If what thou speakest speak not of remedy.

For Juliet love becomes the fountain of courage and strength, thus she says:

Love give me strength! and strength shall help afford.
Farewell, dear father. (Act IV Scene I)

Juliet is disturbed because she is about to be married with Paris. To face the situation she reveals her anguish in her soliloquy:

I have a faint cold fear thrills through my veins
That almost freezes up the heat of life.
I'll call them back again to comfort me.
Nurse!—what should she do here?
My dismal scene I needs must act alone.
Come, vial!
What if this mixture do not work at all?
Shall I be married then tomorrow morning?
No, no! This shall forbid it lie thou there. (Act IV Scene III)

When Juliet comes to her senses, she sees Romeo lying dead there holding a cup, then she too drinks the poison and dies to redeem their love:

Poison, I see, hath been his timeless end,
O churl! drunk all and left no friendly drop
To help me after? I will kiss thy lips.
Haply some poison yet doth hang on them
To make me die with a restorative. Thy lips are warm!
(Act V Scene III)

Sufi is one who is the lover of truth, who by means of love and devotion moves towards the Truth, towards the perfection which all are truly seeking. Sufis' love of the beloved and for the whole creation is portrayed by poets like Hafez and Ebn Faredh and prose writers like Sohrawardi and Ebn 'Arabi'. Such works have not only been a constant source of spiritual guidance and encouragement for Sufis, but have even inspired people not directly involved with the Sufi Path. Hazrat Inayat Khan, a great Sufi mystic belonging to the Classical Mysticism of Sufism in his work *The Dance of the Soul* describes love:

> I have loved in life and I have been loved.
> I have drunk the bowl of poison from the hands of love as nectar and have been raised above life's joy and sorrow.
> My heart, aflame in love, set afire every heart that came in touch with it.
> My heart has been rent and joined again;
> My heart has been broken and again made whole;
> My heart has been wounded and healed again;
> A thousand deaths my heart has died, and thanks be to love, it lives yet.
> I went through hell and saw there love's raging fire,
> and I entered heaven illumined with the light of love.
> I wept in love and made all weep with me;
> I mourned in love and pierced the hearts of men;
> And when my fiery glance fell on the rocks,
> The rocks burst forth as volcanoes.
> The whole world sank in the flood caused by means of my one tear;
> With my deep sigh the earth trembled, and when I cried aloud the name of my beloved,
> I shook the throne of God in heaven.
> I bowed my head low in humility, and on my knees I begged of love,
> "Disclose to me, I pray thee, o love, thy secret."
> She took me gently by my arms and lifted me above the earth, and spoke softly in my ear,

> "My dear one, thou thyself art love, art lover and thyself art the beloved whom thou hast adored." (Internet)

Sahl was the master of al-Husayn Ibn Mansur al-Hallaj, who has become famous for his phrase ana al-haqq, "I am the Creative truth" (often rendered "I am God"), which was later interpreted in a pantheistic sense but is, in fact, only a condensation of his theory of "huwa huwa" (He he"): God loved himself in his essence, and created Adam "in his image." In *The Holy Bible*, we read:

> Then god said, "Let us make humankind in our image, according to our likeness . . . so God created humankind in his image, in the image of God he created them; male and female he created them. (*Genesis* ch. I verses 26-27)

The supreme example of love is also depicted in *The New Testament* of *The Holy Bible*:

> For God so loved the world that he gave his only son, so that everyone who believes in him may not perish but may have eternal life. (St. John 3:16)

Once someone asked Jesus Christ, 'teacher tell me what shall I do to inherit the kingdom of God?' Then Jesus said keep the commandments and summarized the innumerous laws of *The Old Testament* into just two. First, "love your God with all your soul, with all your heart and with all your mind." And the second is similar to the first, "love your neighbour as yourself."

In *All for Love*, love is depicted as a perfect virtue for Antony renounces all—family, friends, country and kingdom—for love's sake. Love is not mere physical passion, it is a virtue: an heroic passion, it kindles in the soul "honour's fire," and so the lover is eager to be worthy of his desire. To be worthy of his beloved, he must be a man of honour, and honour includes all possible moral and spiritual qualities. Heroic love purifies the hero of all base desires and makes him a fit object of admiration.

According to an ardent apostle of Christ, St. Paul, love (charity) is the greatest, cardinal or theological virtue among the seven virtues (faith, hope, love, justice, prudence, temperance, and fortitude).

The Neo-Platonists were acutely aware of the love of God, through the world of senses. They saw in human love a reflection of the divine love. According to them love held the world together. Beauty was the divine idea in the material object and love was the perception of that idea.

During the Elizabethan Age poets and sonneteers wrote on the theme of love. John Donne in his metaphysical poems elucidates the immortal nature of love defined in the Medieval Scholasticism with vivid imagery and analogy.

T. Clifton Longwork author of *The Devil a Monk would Be* in his another work, *The Worship of Love* considers love an all-pervading force and apotheosis of creation, and analytically through myths, symbols and emblems of love presented in many religions in various parts of the world.

There are innumerous, exquisite and beautiful songs on love in the world of music. Here I would like to quote some lines of a song from *With Joyful Lips*, which depicts the supreme form of love:

> Greater love and friendship has no man than this that he die for others, give his life for all.

In all the above references love has been greatly praised and admired that reveal the true nature of love. True love in Shakespearean comedies ennobles mankind. Rosalind, Viola and to a lesser extent, Beatrice, are Shakespeare's images of the best way of love: "They, and in whom they inspire love, are Shakespeare's representation of the office of love to lift mankind to a richer life." The men and women who love truly have become superb representations of human nature. True love is spiritual. It is the union of minds and hearts. The entire atmosphere in Shakespearean comedies is surcharged with love. It was a legacy perhaps from the Platonic love. It was considered superior to all virtues. A sound guaranteed love was an excuse for any betrayal of friendship or dereliction of duty. It was a law unto itself that overbore all other laws.

Romeo and Juliet celebrates one of the most kernel emotions of mankind—love. Both Romeo and Juliet are presented by Shakespeare as great archetypes of love. For them love is the highest thing in this world. They treat each other as God. The union that they aspire for is not the ordinary union of two bodies, rather the union of two souls with perfect love. So the approach they adopt can be related to the approach of Christianity and Sufism in which a person tries to unite oneself with God through prayer, meditation and practice of love (charity), believing that the union will redeem the soul and lead to divine oneness. The same trait has been reflected by the Indian poets of the Bhakti Movement in which Meera, Surdas and others treat God as lover and not as deity. Side by side Romeo and Juliet both are silent sufferers. They never abandon any pain that comes in their way, being troubled by the people around them. The death to Romeo and Juliet does not mean the way it means to others; it is a way ahead towards the ultimate goal. It is believed in Christianity that death is the gateway to new life or a life of eternity. It leads to a new sphere of life. So, they withstand whatever obstacle comes in their way of love.

Shakespeare has been able to illustrate the immense power of love. A person having true passion of love in one's bosom overcomes every tempest. Herein lies the genius of Shakespeare to sublimate love to the level of divine element, which he has done time and again in his plays as well as sonnets. He has glorified love, idealized love, rather we can say deified love and he has made love the synonym of God.

Bibliography

Bhatia, P., *Romeo and Juliet*, UBS, New Delhi, 2012.

Dominic, V. *With Joyful Lips*, St. Pauls Publication, Bombay, 1995.

Kumar, S., *A History of English Literature*, Lakshmi Narain Agarwal, Agra, 2006.

Longwork, T.C., *The Worship of Love*, Sarup, New Delhi, 2012.

Nelson, T. *The Holy Bible*, New Revised Std. Version Bible, Catholic Edition, Theological Publications in India, Bangalore, 1994.

Internet Notes, www.encyclopedia-ofreligion.org/Sufism.html

Shakespeare in Indian Popular Culture: A Critique of the Film *Omkara*

DEEPAK KUMAR RAI
Res. Sch., Banaras Hindu University

For the last four and half centuries, Shakespeare has remained close to many cultures of the world and his plays have been read and staged in different cultures and various historical circumstances. They have been translated into many languages and, in the last two centuries, projected on the big and the small screen. Shakespeare, in other words, turns out to be amazingly malleable and adaptable to the needs of changing societies. His genius permanently shaped the English language, while his knowledge of the human mind and heart speaks to us across the years. In the words of his friend and rival playwright Ben Jonson, "He was not of an age, but for all time."

His name has become synonymous with the two words 'great literature'. He seems to be everywhere: he is quoted and adapted daily in newspaper headlines and in commercials for a wide range of projects. In British and American schools, he is the only compulsory author in the National Curriculum and in Advanced Level English Literature. In the views of Maynard Mack, "Shakespeare is the only writer in world literature who actually comes close to belonging to the world." Shakespeare still has a sort of pervasive influence on the English language and on Western and global culture.

Talking about multiple adaptations, it's not only legendary Indian authors that inspire us, but also all the plays of William Shakespeare have been generously adapted over the years in

Bollywood. He was one of the greatest writers ever and one of the best script writers known all over the world. His abstract genius was impeccable. His works like *Romeo and Juliet, Macbeth, Julius Caesar, and Othello* have made history. Many a creative talent, be he/she a composer, a painter, a novelist or a film-maker, has approached Shakespeare's plays for getting inspiration from him. His writing brought the characters to life.

The world-famous literary works of the Bard of Avon have for decades inspired Bollywood films but no one credited Shakespeare. He is finally getting due credit as the inspiration of many Hindi films after decades of no recognition and blatant plagiarism. *Comedy of Errors*, one of Shakespeare's earlier plays written way back in 1592-94 was adapted into two Hindi films *Do Duni Chaar* in 1968 and then *Angoor* in 1982 and one Kannada film titled *Ulta Palta.* Although these films were successful yet no one publicized their Shakespearean adaptations till Vishal Bhardwaj came along.

The well-known film director Vishal Bhardwaj's choice of social milieu for his meditations on Shakespeare's tragic tales of kings and generals continues to be interesting. He adapted two plays of Shakespeare, namely *Macbeth* as *Maqbool* and *Othello* as *Omkara* in Bollywood flavor, and both were well appreciated by the critics and audience. In setting both *Maqbool* and *Omkara* among criminals, he simultaneously draws on the legacy of the gangster film as a vehicle of high drama and intense emotion, and pointedly highlights a reality in today's India. Vishal adapted Shakespeare's 17th century classic *Othello* in his 2006 film *Omkara* which won him commercial as well as critical success. The film is a tragic love story and above all depicts the varied negative human emotions that accompany the feeling of love.

A brilliantly executed adaptation of Shakespeare's *Othello, Omkara* has been adapted extremely well by Vishal. The style with which Vishal has managed to adapt the film for Indian audiences is simply remarkable by readjusting the story of *Othello* by locating it in the interiors of Uttar Pradesh so a very local Indian flavour fills the European framework. But it is difficult to imagine any equivalence between the Venice-Cyprus of *Othello* and the U.P. of *Omkara*. If we say that this rural Indian setting is an appropriate translation of the original setting of *Othello*, there is nothing to justify it.

Vishal has adapted every single aspect of the film to blend in with the setting including the location, costumes, sets, dialogues, accent and even the mannerisms of his characters. Vishal tells the story with extreme finesse, the flow of events, the depth of the characters and finally the culmination. On the surface the film depicts the tragic end of a love story but the way Vishal depicts the several shades of love, the passion, the jealousy, the rage, the betrayal, the manipulation and even the grey aspects of his characters is simply astounding.

Omkara is a modern retelling of *Othello* where all the pieces fall into place more or less on cue. The film's characters are given names that either begin with the same letter as the originals, or sound like those names. It deals with everything the original story dealt with, including morality, faith, doubt, love, betrayal and deception.

The powerful title character Omkara Shukla; Omi (Ajay Devgan) has the kind of glowering, brooding presence one expects of an Othello, as a Bahubali. He is the right hand of a politician Bhaisahab (Naseeruddin Shah) somewhere in Hindi belt of north India. In the beginning of the movie he elopes with beautiful Dolly (Kareena Kapoor). After some time, when he is promoted in the political hierarchy, he appoints, Kesu Firangi (Vivek Oberoi) as his successor instead of Langda Tyagi (Saif Ali Khan) who had been faithfully working with him for about fifteen years, leading to jealousy and tragedy. Langda clearly believes he is entitled to the position bestowed to Kesu, but his relationship with Omkara makes the sight so shattering that he responds with such cruel revenge. An innocent victim of these machinations is Dolly (Kareena Kapoor), whom Omkara loves but comes to distrust through no fault of her own. Langda smitten with jealousy and vengeance spins a plot wherein he convinces Omkara that his beloved Dolly has an affair with Kesu. The end is tragic. Between these characters a very important character is that of Indu (Konkona Sen Sharma), who in the end reveals the truth to Omkara. But it's too late! Needless to say, Omkara is Othello, Dolly is Desdemona, Kesu is Cassio and Langda Tyagi is Iago while Indu is Emilia.

Vishal's adaptation of *Othello* is remarkable. *Omkara* is a realistic, different and intellectual film. The Omkara-Langda relationship is the film's pivot. Iago's Machiavellian jealousy in Othello is transposed into a state of stunning bedroom politics. The hanky of Othello is replaced by a traditional 'Kamarbandh' that Omi gifts Dolly. Langda's wife Indu (Emilia, Konkana Sen Sharma) steals the gift of love as her husband had always urged her to do the same. How Tyagi uses this article of faith in hitting the nail in the Coffin of Trust forms the crux of the story.

Langda, in *Omkara*, is the parallel character of Iago in *Othello*, and, as far as the general plot is concerned, the film creates a close analogy between the two characters. The story is the same: Langda is angered by Omkara's choice of Kesu over himself for general, just as Iago is angered by Othello's choice of Cassio over himself for lieutenant. The first way in which the film lessens the evil we see in Langda is by allowing the audience to empathize with his situation. In *Othello*, there is no sympathy felt for Iago, throughout the play. From the beginning to the end he is seen as a villain, with no room to doubt.

Such a dark play, well handled with each character is brought to life. One feels for Othello, but Shakespeare's plays are known for their hard hitting truths and sad ends to beautifully presented characters. Still, I think that there was a lapse in the development of characters of Omkara (Ajay Devgan) and Kesu

(Vivek Oberoi). In the play, Othello was a moor and dark-skinned and hence, he had all the reasons to believe that Desdemona (here Dolly) could be attracted towards Cassio, a white European. However, in the film I don't see a big contrast between the characters of Omkara and Kesu. However, otherwise Kesu's character is shown to be so subdued that this subtle contrast doesn't make such a big difference as it does in Shakespeare's *Othello*.

This adaptation of *Othello* is a tremendous one, as its purpose is to make Shakespeare available not only to the Indian people but also attuned to the sensibility of a non-English-educated audience, differing only in little plot details. Vishal takes care of the smallest possible detail for the adaptation of *Othello*. The dark-skinned Othello is presented here as Omkara (Ajay Devgan) who is wearing dark to get a darker complexion. To highlight the contrast between his dark skin and Dolly's fair complexion, some nice dialogues have been delivered through Indu where she teases the couple saying, "koyle ke lote me doodh."

Vishal has incorporated commercial as well as realistic aspects in his film even though the subject is dark and brooding. There is everything in the film, drama, romance, song and dance, emotions and finally tragedy. *Omkara* is not an ordinary work of art. It's a full-blown treatise on the politics of the human heart. Male and female bonding is paramount to Bhardwaj's plot. In his amazing understanding of both Shakespeare's tragic resonance and UP's ruinous politics, the director is next to none. This tale finds Shakespeare's *Othello* transplanted to gritty modern India. *Omkara*, like *Othello*, is not a comforting, uplifting story. Still, it's hard to escape the fact that *Omkara*, like *Othello*, is not a story where women get many good lines.

Works Cited

Ben Jonson. "To the memory of my beloved, The Author Master William Shakespeare: And what he hath left us." *The Works of Ben Jonson*, vol. 3. London: Chatto & Windus, 1910. 287-89.

Maynard Mack. "Everybody's Shakespeare," Lincoln: University of Nebraska Press, 1994.

Vikram Singh Thakur. "Shakespeare Reception in India and The Netherlands until the Early Twentieth Century," *CLC Web: Comparative Literature and Culture* 14.2 (2012): http://docs.lib.purdue.edu/clcweb/vol14/iss2/4

Miriam Huntley. "Villains—A Comparison of the Antagonists of *Omkara* and *Othello.*" 21F.011. Web November 10, 2006.

Daniel Montgomery. "Omkara—Vishal Bhardwaj" Web. August 09, 2011. http://www.culturazzi.org/cinema/omkara-vishal-Bhardwaj

"Evaluating and Analyzing Omkara and Othello". Anti Essays. http://www.antiessays.com/free-essays/88061.html

"Omkara—Othello and the Dirty Business of Politics (a film review) http://www.lehigh.edu/~amsp /2006/07/omkara-othello-and-dirty-business-of.html

Faridoon Shahryar. "Omkara—Omkara Will Make Shakespeare Happy" *India Glitz*. July 28, 2006.

Movie Review, Omkara. ApunKaChoice.Com. <http://www.apunkachoice.com/movies/mov755/omkara-review.html>

Ron Ahluwalia. Movie review—Omkara. Web. Planet Bollywood http://www.planetbollywood.com/displayReview.php?id=07300603271 0

Rethinking Shakespeare in Hindi and Bhojpuri Literature

ABHA Singh
Dyal Singh Evening College, University of Delhi

Shakespeare's greatness and pre-eminence as a dramatist is universally recognized. It is universally accepted that Shakespeare is not of an age but of all ages, not of one country but of all countries. Though his plays were written more than four hundred years ago and reflect tastes, customs and transitions of Shakespeare's own age yet they are as popular today as before: "Shakespeare's plays are part of a worldwide theatrical repertory, and so sustain critical tension animating dramatic performativity today."[1]

His plays have been translated into almost all the important languages of the world and most of them have been filmed and staged through different media. In recent years the status of the translation of literary texts and that of the translator has changed radically. The translator is no longer expected to draw only on linguistic skill, but also an artistic and cultural awareness of the target readers or audiences. The only way of being 'faithful' to Shakespeare in the intercultural context is to relocate him fully. The reason why Shakespeare became more popular in India is that India is a country with diverse languages and literary culture that could assimilate Shakespeare in various ways. Shakespeare came to us at a moment when our society and culture were in need of a new direction and change.

Shakespearean production in Calcutta and other big cities of India revived the interest of the Indian people on stage and drama. The Shakespeare stage being "a raised bare platform, jutting out some considerable distance among the audience, so that the group of players was seen from any points of view,"[2] drew the attention of the Indian people towards the medieval stage which had many things in common with Shakespeare. The influence of both his style and dramatic production led to a revival of the great dramatic tradition in India both in literary and folk form which flourished from the ancient classical time down to the medieval. The post-war theatre in India has been largely influenced by the western theatre especially in setting and technique, latest scientific devices in sound effect and creating scenic beauty, so it would be difficult to state precisely how much debt it owes to Shakespearean Stage. It would be beneficial first to consider the staging of Shakespeare's play in original by European as well as Indian and then to analyze its influence on the Hindi stage. The Shakespeare production in India in original began with the establishment of the 'Calcutta Theatre' in 1776, where Richard III (25 January and 1 February, 1788), Henry IV, Part I (8 February, 1788, Henry IV, Part II (22 February 1788) [Calcutta Gazette, 5 Feb and 28 Feb, 1788] were main among Shakespearean plays which were performed and staged. In 1789 *Julius Caesar* was acted in Mrs. Bristow's Theatre and in 1797 (5 May) Catherine and Petruchio, a comedy, was performed.[3] The Chowringhee Theatre played *Henry IV*, on 23 July 1814 and *Merry Wives of Windsor* on 25 September 1818. The Sans-Souci Theatre staged *Othello* on 24 April 1844 and also on 17 August and September 12, 1848. There were several attempts too made to put Shakespeare on Stage but these are some of the ample evidences on record. In these plays all the performers were Indian. Besides these there are several Shakespearean performers and their troupes who visited India and staged Shakespeare's plays. In November 1911 and 1912, the well-known Shakespearean actor Mr. Allan Wilkie with Miss Frediswyde Hunter Watts came to India and performed *Macbeth*,

Romeo and Juliet, *Hamlet*, *Julius Caesar*, *Merry Wives of Windsor*, *The Merchant of Venice*, *Twelfth Night* and *Othello*. Mr. Matheson Lang and his coadjutor Mr. Hutin Britton entertained their audiences in London as well as visited India in 1911-12 to perform some of the plays of Shakespeare. These performances not only popularized Shakespeare in India but also induced Indian students to stage Shakespearean plays. In 1956 students of B.R. College, Agra requested the visiting English company to enact *Macbeth* as they themselves intended to perform this on their college stage. Norman Marshall liked their performance and remarked, "Perhaps rather surprisingly, I found in India the reaction of the audience to some aspects of the plays was more Elizabethan than it is in England (Marshall: 91-110)."[4]

Dozens of companies sprang up across the country, all financed by Parsi businessmen who were theatre buffs. Muslims, Anglo-Indians and some Hindus joined the companies but the organizational reins remained largely in Parsi hands. For almost a century, the dramas staged by these companies were the primary form of dramatic entertainment consistently available to urban audiences in greater India. They exerted a major influence on Marathi and Gujarati theatres as well as on new drama in Hindi, Bengali, Tamil and other regional languages. This Shakespearean vogue gave rise to the Parsi Theatre which may be regarded as a parent of the Hindi stage. Along with the original plays based on the *Mahabharata*, the *Ramayana*, and History, the adaptations of Shakespeare's plays were also performed by them. It was vulgarity and somewhat disorderliness of the Parsi theatres that Bhartendu Harishchandra criticized in 1883 and thought to bring revolution in the Hindi stage.[5]

Balkrishna Bhatt also criticized it for its vulgarity and immorality.[6] As a reaction against the Parsi stage, Bhartendu formed his own troupe at Banaras which staged its play, Shitla Prasad Tripati's *Janaki Mangal*, in 1868. It was followed by many other performances. Bhartendu Harishchandra's *Nil Devi*, *Bharata Durdasha*, *Andher Nagri*, were performed between 1869 and 1885. The other playwrights, whose plays were enacted, were Badri Narain Chaudhri (*Bharat Durdasha*), Shirinivas Das (*Sanyogita Swayamvar* and *Randhir aur Prem Mohini*), Radha Charan Goswami, Balakrishna Bhatt and so many others. Varanasi had many theatres: Banaras Theater, Bhartendu Nayak Mandali, Nagari Natak Mandali. Shakespearean plays too found its place on this amateur stage. The translations of Shakespeare's play were also staged, *King Lear* was translated by Lala Sitaram. Little Theatre Group of New Delhi enacted Bachchan's verse translation of *Macbeth* in Dec. 1958 at Fine Arts Theatre. In January 1968 another Hindi Translation by Bachchan, that is, *Othello* was staged at Fine Art Theatre. Jai Sankar Prasad was a man of genius who possessed the sound knowledge of English and had read Shakespeare's work along with a copy of Plutarch. As Marlow paved way for Shakespeare, Bhartendu paved way for Jai Shankar Prasad. *Prayashchita* (1914) is the first drama of Prasad written under the influence of Shakespeare. The present paper will study how Shakespearean plays provided an incentive to Hindi and Bhojpuri Drama and also helped the Hindi stage to pass from the crude farcical theatre of the folk tradition to a more respectable stage with proper dramatic effect. The age of Bhartendu (1850-1885) was an age of literary renaissance; various forms of tradition and convention gave way to modernity. Bhartendu played the leading role in assimilating Shakespeare into Hindi drama. The literary public also felt a sort of aversion towards rigidity and artificiality of the classical Sanskrit rules. His knowledge of English made him realize the obsoleteness of classical Sanskrit rules e.g. 'prakari', 'vilobhan', 'asish', 'five sandhis' which was brought forward by Bharat Muni in his *Natayashatra*. According to him, a play cannot be natural and realistic unless it holds the 'mirror up to nature' he liked

'Swabhavik Rachna'. In Bhartendu *Nil Devi* we find some traits of Shakespearean tragedy.

Lala Shrinivas Das (1851-1887)[7] was a contemporary of Bhartendu Harishchandra and his work shows that he did a thorough study of Shakespeare. His play *Randhir aur Prem Mohini* resembles and recalls *Romeo and Juliet* in several episodes. The main story of the play is: The king of Surat and the king of Patan are hostile to each other. Prem Mohini, a beautiful daughter of king of Surat, and Randhir, the son of the King of Patan, falls in love and when the time for Prem Mohini's Swayamvara comes , her preference for Randhir leads to a bloody battle in which Prem Mohini's brother, Ripudaman, is killed trying to save his friend Randhir. Randhir somehow staggers to the palace and dies there in the lap of his beloved. Prem Mohini stabs herself and falls by the side of her lover. After the tragic end of lovers, reconciliation takes place between the two kings and the order is made to erect statues of the lovers. This play is closely modelled on Shakespeare's play *Romeo and Juliet*. This play is the first tragedy in Hindi drama. The tragic conception of the play had been inspired by Shakespeare's tragic idea. The tragedy proceeds with inherent flaw in the character of Randhir. This flaw is present in him from the very beginning. Due to this flaw he leaves the kingdom of his father, and is bent upon to punish innocent Choubeji without investigating about the real culprit and at the end implicates himself in a battle single-handed with the king of Surat and his supporters.

There are some scenes in *Randhir and Prem Mohini* where we get echoes of the 'balcony scene' in Act III, scene iv in *Romeo and Juliet*. Randhir and Prem Mohini meet in an orchard. After seeing Mohini from a distance he says: "*Isa samaya isa pushpa vatika mein ye parkash kaisa ho raha hai. Suryodaya ka samaya to abhi nahin hua.*" (III.iv. 92) These lines seem to have been inspired by the following lines by Romeo: "But, soft, what light through yonder window breaks? It is the east, and Juliet is the sun arise, fair sun" (III.ii. 2-4). Later in the same scene Randhir says: "*Aba Kuchha mere mana ko dhariya dene ka bhi to upaya karo"* (III.iv) echoes the following speech by Romeo: "O, wilt thou leave me so unsatisfied?" (II: ii) In fifth scene of the third act of *Romeo and Juliet* opens in Juliet Chamber. The fifth scene of the third act of *Randhir and Prem Mohini* takes place in Prem Mohini's Palace. When Randhir wants to take leave from Mohini she wants to detain him:

> *Randhir: (Akasa ki ora dekh kar) He priye dekho suryodaya ka samaya ho gaya dipak ki jyoti manda pada gai, har ke moti sitala ho gaye, pakshi chahchahane lage aur, kamal ke chikne patton se osa ki bunden motiyan ki ladi ke saman dhalakne lagin, ab tum jane do to main bhi jakar snana karu.*
>
> *Premmohini: Na pran pyare abhi suryodaya ka samaya nahi hua. Aapke tej se dipak ki jyoti manda pada gai aur pushpo ki sitalta se moti thande ho gaye. Pakshi nahin chahchahate. Ratri ke karan mithe mithe suron se koyal bolti hai, Kamala ke patton para osa ki bunden nahin dhalaktee mere kapolon par ansu bah aaye hain.*

A similar situation is found in Act III scene v, line 1-16 in *Romeo and Juliet.* Juliet wants to detain Romeo:

> Juliet: Wilt thou be gone? It is not yet near day: It was the nightingale, and not the lark. That pierc'd the fearful hollow of thine ear; nightly she sings on yon pomegranate tree: Believe me, love, it was the nightingale.
>
> Romeo: It was the lark the herald of the morn,
> No nightingale: look, love, what envious streaks
> Do lace the severing clouds in yonder east:
> Night's candles are burnt out and jocund day
> Stands tiptoe on the misty mountain tops
> I must be gone and live, or stay and die.
> Juliet: Yon light is not daylight, I know it, I:
> It is some meteor that sun exals
> To be to this night a torch bearer,
> And light thee on thy way to Mantua:

Therefore stay yet: thou need'st not to be gone.

In both these plays fine conceit has been expressed through different symbol. Shrinivas Das in his play *Randhir aur Prem Mohini* bears out Shakespeare's influence in respect of theme, the conception of conflict and also what was prohibited in Sanskrit dramaturgy, he had tried to introduce e.g. death of hero, battle which was not permitted in Indian classical rules of drama.

Jai Shankar Prasad was a man of genius. His emergence in Hindi drama is like Shakespeare's emergence on Elizabethan scene. He was not only the man of translation but he possessed the sound knowledge of English and read Shakespeare's work. Mishra quotes: "A copy of Shakespeare's complete works was found in his library after his death. He also possessed a copy of Plutarch's *Lives*. Prasad had also referred to Shakespeare in his essays which throws light on his comprehensive study and a proper understanding of Shakespeare."[10] Jai Shankar Prasad under the influence of Shakespeare dramatized the theme from Indian history. His *Ajatshatru* (1922) bears out a strong impact of Shakespeare's dramatic technique. Prasad shows the two feelings in the character of Ajatshatru alone like Shakespeare. At the beginning of the play *Ajatshatru* we see King Bimbsar gives up his power of throne in favour of his son Ajatshatru and begins to live the life of a hermit with his chief queen Vaswi. Ajatshatru under influence of his mother Chhalna and a Buddhist Devdatta torture his father in various ways. This reminds us of King Lear's mental agony caused by his two daughters among whom he had divided his kingdom. Prasad makes Ajatshatru realize his misdeeds and later shows his love towards King Bimbsar like Cordelia.

In Shakespeare, the sub-plot serves as a parallel or contrast to or a commentary upon the main plot and heightens the effect of the main story. In *King Lear*, Edmund-Edgar story runs parallel to the main story of Goneril, Regan and Cordelia and both have the theme of filial ingratitude. In the play the *Ajatshatru* too we find parallel sub-plot of Virudhak ingratitude towards his father Prasenajita runs with the main plot of Ajatshatru's ingratitude towards his father Bimbsar. Like Ajatshatru, Virudhak too feels penitent and is reconciled to his father. This shows the alteration of two feelings in both Prasad and Shakespeare play. In some of the characters individually we find the influence of Shakespeare's character, as in King Lear we see the same reflective nature and the same fury in Bimbisar. Bimbisar's long speech in Act II, sc.vi, p. 86 resembles King Lear's long soliloquy in Act III,Sc.ii, line 1-9 and 14-24.

> Bimbsar: *Jivaka ab tuma visrama karo. Ab aur koi samachar sunane ki ichha nahin hai. Sansar bhar men vidroha, sangharsha, aur pratarana hai. Yahi sab tum sunaoge, aisa mujhe nishchaya ho gaya. Jane do. Ek shital nishwas lekar tum vishwa ke watya chakra se alag ho jao aur ispar parlay ke surya ki kirano se tap kar galte hue gile lohe ki varha hone do. Avishvas ki andhiyon ko sarapat daudane do. Prithvi ke praniyo me anyaya badhe jisase dridha hokar log anisvaravadi ho jaye, aur pratidin nai samasya hal karte karte kritaghna jiva murkhata ki dhul udave—aur vishwa bhar men isi par eka unamatta attahas ho. (unmatta bhav se jata hai)*

Bimbsar is full of rage for the ingratitude which his son had shown towards him. This soliloquy of Bimbsar strikes us with the passion and fury of King Lear in Act 3.ii. 1-9

> Blow, winds, and crack your cheeks, rage, blow,
> You cataract and hurricanes, sprout
> Till you have drenched our steeples, drowned the cock:
> You sulphurous and thought executing fires,
> Vaunt-couriers to oak cleaving thunderbolts,
> Singe my white head, and thou, all-shaking thunder,
> Strike flat thick rotundity o'the world,
> Crack nature's moulds, all germens spill at once
> That ungrateful man

Both these passages from Prasad's *Ajatshatru* and Shakespeare's *King Lear* indicate the similar emotion, both being tormented by the ingratitude of their children and they call upon different elements to be unkind. Shakespeare's belief in fate and destiny had been shown in both Bimbsar and King Lear. There is a force of destiny behind every activity of man. Prasad drew inspiration from Shakespeare. He regards destiny as the force behind all human actions and regards man as the plaything of God. As Bimbsar says:

> Aakash ke neele patra par ujwal aksharo se likhe adrisht ke likh ab dheere dheere lupt hone lage hain, tabhi to manushya prabhat samajhne lagata hai, aur jeevan sangram me pravit hokar anek aakand-tandav karata hai; phir bhi prakriti use andhakar ki gufa me le jakar uska shanty maya, rahasyapurna bhagya ka chittha samjhane ka prayatna karati hai. (*Ajatshatru* I.ii. p. 27)

Shakespeare expresses such feeling of man being a slave through Lear. "I am even the natural fool of fortune" (IV.vi. 195-96). Further in the same Act, Gloucester says: "As flies to wanton boys, are we to th'gods; They kill us for their sports." (IV.I. 36-37) Like Shakespeare he also calls destiny the 'wheel' (chakra) and man the 'instrument' (yantra) of fortune. "Mein us adrisht shakti ka yantra hun. Vahajo mere saath hai mujhase koi kama karana chahata hai" (III.iv). But the idea of Edgar regarding destiny is different. He believes that the Gods are just and punish us for our faults. There is ambiguity of the idea regarding destiny which had been found in both *King Lear* and *Ajatshatru*.

As far as the portrayal of character is concerned Prasad's character Virudhak seems to have been inspired by the character of Edmund. Edmund is bastard son of Gloucester while Virudhak is "Dasiputra." The intriguing nature of both Edmund and Virudhak can be seen in the sub-plot. As a lover also they resemble: Edmund professes love for both the sisters, Goneril and Regan, Virudhak too makes love with Mallika and Shyama at the same time. Like Shakespearean soliloquies Prasad also provides us with soliloquies in his play to reveal internal thought and feeling of the character. The soliloquies of Bimbsar, Jivak, and Vajira shed light on the wider and mortal aspect of life. Jaganath Prasad Sharma remarks: "the structure of the plot in *Ajatshatru* does not lend itself well to the Sanskrit dramaturgical plot division into the five stages like 'arambh'-'yatna'-'praptyashya'-'niyatapti'-'phalagam' but is based on western technique of plot construction for example exposition, complication, climax, denouement and catastrophe."[8] This shows how Jai Shankar Prasad got influenced from his study of Shakespeare.

Bharat Muni's *Natyashastra* denotes that there was great theatrical tradition in ancient India. After 11th century, the theatrical tradition in classical drama declined and gave way to folk theatres like 'Ramlila', 'Raslila', 'Nautanki', 'Yatra' etc. The change of theatrical tradition took place after the rise of Muslim power in India. The folk plays were precisely like the "Improvista Commedia" of the Italians. The folk theatre could not give birth to any great dramatic tradition in Hindi in the medieval time. Though the other form of art had flourished at the Mogul Courts but theatre had never enjoyed favourable reception and style. These rural performances had something very vital about them and it had been aptly quoted by Nicoll, who wrote about the earlier rural performance in Britain: "There is a freshness of fancy here, a free treatment of material, a rich fund of humour, and at times true sense of the profound and the tragic."[9]

In the Bhojpuri theatre too we find such rural performances. It was more of folklore with folk music and poems. Shakespeare came to us at a moment when our society and culture were in need of new direction and change. Bhartendu Harishchandra who is considered the father of Hindi Literature was highly influenced by the tone and style of Bhojpuri speaking region.

Rahul Sanskrityanan had called him "Uncut Diamond." Legendry cultural personality Bhikhari Thakur was often called the Shakespeare of Bhojpuri literature for he led the renaissance in Bhojpuri folk music. Though there is no such translation of Shakespearean plays in Bhojpuri language but it does give us prose and poetic variations of Shakespeare and registers the emotion of that time. Though some critics remarked that "it does not reflect authentic Shakespeare" but when we read the biography of Thakur, some element of theme and emotions visible make it coherent and forces 'within' and 'without' which produces "other Shakespeare" in him. In Bhikhari Thakur's stage presentation Shakespearean stories like brothers' rivalry, widow problem, migration, marriage of daughters etc. is found but the plays cannot in the strict sense be seen as real performances of Shakespeare play. Shakespearean nuances can be explored in his plays. Shakespeare who had imperialistic imposition is now being recreated and is becoming legitimized and localized in Indian society. Shakespeare empowers all races, location and culture to read him in their own light. The relocation of Shakespeare into a home-grown folk form and popular culture was not an end in itself but a part of larger purpose.

Bhikhari Thakur, like Shakespeare, was born in a lower class. He was born in a barber-family on 18 December 1887 at Kutubpur (Diyara) Village in Saran District, now in Bihar province. He also did not get proper education like Shakespeare. He is best known for the creation of the twentieth century theatre form 'Bidesia'. Bhikari Thakur belonged to the backward caste, who abandoned home and hearth to form a group of actors who dealt with issues of contestation: between the traditional and the modern, between urban and rural, between the haves and the have-nots and so on. Appreciative native Bhojpuri audiences consider Bhikari Thakur as the incomparable founder father, propagator and exponent par excellence of this form. He was a folk poet, a folk singer, a folk dancer and actor.

In nineteenth century when Bhikhari Thakur was struggling to make ends meet, he was impressed and inspired by movements carried out then by famous Bengali social reformers like Raja Ram Mohan Roy, Ram Krishna Paramhans & Swami Vivekanand. This simple and poor young man, quiet impressed by Bengal's 'punarjagran andolan', returned to his native place Qutubpur, and noticing his society's problems minutely was enriched and enlightened with ideas on every social level that can be seen and felt in his compositions. He took 'the Renaissance spirit' positively and decided to deliver it to the Bhojpuri society through songs, poems and drama. Possibility lies that during his visit to Calcutta he must have seen some of the performances of Shakespeare as he was influenced by the "open air jatra stage." May be Bhikhari Thakur's theatre was haunted by the presence of Shakespearean elements in his play which places him in the category of Shakespeare.

Shakespeare was really good at the theme of brother rivalry. Apart from *Hamlet* you can also see it in *Twelfth Night* and *King Lear*. A constant theme of Shakespeare's plays, the falling out and coming together of brothers, can be found in Bhikhari Thakur's play too. It was this relationship which Bhikhari Thakur understood and mistrusted in many ways. He certainly recognized the deep divisions and rivalries between brothers in *Bhai-Virodh*. Thakur deals with the theme of opposition of brothers which is a very prominent feature of Bihar's rural society. Three brothers are separated due to lack of confidence and respect for each other when instigated by a person outside their family. However, at the end they realize the importance of living together.

Beti-Bechwa, a play by Thakur is considered a very progressive play. Bhikari Thakur through this play criticizes the widespread custom of selling young girls in marriage to much older men. This custom prevailed in Bhojpuri-speaking areas until recently. The protagonist is a young girl whose father sells her to an older person. Shakespeare in his play *Taming of the Shrew* emphasizes on economic considerations to determine who marries whom; marriage becomes a transaction involving the transfer of money. Lucentio wins Bianca's heart, but he is given permission to marry her only after he is able to convince Baptista that he is fabulously rich. Had Hortensio offered more money, he would have married Bianca, regardless of whether she loved Lucentio.

Almost all Thakur's plays took theme from the society like Shakespeare did but were moulded in his new progressive and revolutionary style.

The theory of human nature being a compound of these four elements in varying proportions has been the basis of human psychology in Shakespearean Drama. Man was subjected to the rare harmonies of these four elements and their never-ending discords. This view of human nature had a great appeal to the Indian mind. This line from Bhikari Thakur's *Bedesia* is a wonderful example of fine conceit expressed through different symbols "*javan kua ke jal ukha me pataval jala, ohi kuan ka jal se maricha patella, uhe jal ukha ke meetha aur maricha ke teet kael dela*," it reflects nature and how it affects human beings: "*jinke rahi bhavana jaise. Prabhu murti dekhee tinha jaise.*"

The story of Bhikhari Thakur's *Vidhwa-Vilap* is about how widows were treated within their homes. The story reflects the hatred and seclusion a widow had to suffer in brahminical society for no fault of her own: "kavan kasur keile, ghar se nikalan gaile." Further how her property had been snatched and is driven out of village by her relatives. It reminds us of Shakespeare's sonnet no 9 and 97:

> The world will be thy widow and still weep
> That thou no forms of thee hast left behind,
> When every private widow well may keep
> By children's eyes, her husband's shape in mind:
> Look what an unthrift in the world doth spend. (Sonnet 9)

This sonnet reflects agony of a widow that if you happen to die childless, the entire world will mourn for you like a wife who's lost her husband. The world will see you as widow and weep for you.

> Like widow'd wombs after their lords' decease:
> Yet this abundant issue seemed to me
> But hope of orphans, and unfathered fruit;
> For summer and his pleasures wait on thee. (Sonnet 97)

Shakespeare employed the pathetic fallacy, attribution of human characteristic or emotion to element of nature or inanimate objects in sonnet 98:

> From you have I been absent in the spring,
> When proud-pied April (dressed in all his trim) . . .
> Yet seemed it winter still, and you away,
> As with your shadow I with these did play.

The speaker frequently employs the pathetic fallacy, associating his absence from young man to the freezing days in December and reunion to a pregnant spring. Bhikhari Thakur too like Shakespeare employs such pathetic fallacy in his play *Bedesia:* It is dark midnight of 'bhadra mas' Pyari Sundari a female protagonist is in deep thought:

> *Bhado darsavat, aadha rat hoi javat, badi teras pari javat: bund jhamj-3 jhamkavat ba*
> *Gherat ghanghor, jhingur-dadur machavat shor, damini dal saji saji, cham-3 chamkavat ba*
> *Purva pavan aavat, sansanavat, sarmavat, man bhavat naikhe sarag, dum-3dumkavat ba*
> *Kahat 'bhikhari', bhari jari janvavat, tum taruni ke tabiyat bhitar bum-3 bumkavat ba*
> *O samay me pyari sundari kahi ke rohatari?*
> *jania makania me, kevariya:dahakat bari barambar I*
> *piya ghare rahitan, javan javan chahitan; kahitan karati taiyari*
> (25)

There are other devices like the use of dramatic irony, use of pathetic fallacy, personification of natural objects which recalls Shakespeare in Bhikhari Thakur's play.

Shakespeare's cross-dressing throws light on the absence of women and problem of female impersonation. The part of female characters was therefore played by young boys who appeared on the stage in foppish and gaudy female costumes. In 'Jatra' and tradition of 'tamasha' too men performed as female impersonators. The practice of using male impersonators remained the established convention of Indian Drama in the 19th century all over the country and continued till 1930 in many areas. Indian regions are known for particular styles. Gujarat for the 'Bhavi' and Maharashtra for the 'Tamasha' both emphasizing comedy and satire. Bengal for 'jatra' whose focus was on dialogue, Kerala for 'kathakali' which focused on dance, the 'khayal' of Uttar Pradesh and Rajasthan, and the 'nautanki' of Bihar and U.P. that specialized in song. 'Nautanki' form is informal and improvisational, usually with an all-male cast. In Bhikhari Thakur's play also we find all male cast (unlike Sanskrit drama which had female actors). The musician remains on stage in full view of the audience as they would for an Indian play. Dholak, harmonium, like santoor was used. It seems Bhikhari Thakur got influenced by "Jatra" and also by some of the earliest Shakespearean adaptation and productions in Calcutta like *Rudrapal* (*Macbeth*) staged at Great National Theatre on 31 Oct. 1874 and *Bhim Singha* (*Othello*) at Bengal theatre on 27 Feb 1875. All these performances had men acting female roles.

Bhikhari Thakur like Shakespeare brought new revolution in the field of theatre. He was best known for his creation of the twentieth century theatre. He was a barber (a backward) who abandoned home and hearth to form a group of actors who dealt with issues of confrontation through plays: between the traditional and the modern, between the urban and rural, between have and have-nots. When asked why he took to theatre, Bhikari answered, "I used to watch Ramlila and Raslila. When in Ramlila Vyas ji gave sermons to people; I also thought I could also give sermons to my people." (5) This was the reason why educated Bhojpuri people heralded him as the Shakespeare of Bhojpuri literature. There was an affinity between the Elizabethan and the Indian temperament which made Shakespeare readily acceptable to the Indians audiences. The need was felt to re-play Shakespeare for the 'common man'. And thus started the translation and localization of Shakespeare.

NOTES

1. W.B. Worthen, *Shakespeare and the Force of Modern Performance*, 2003:117.
2. Walter Raleigh, *Shakespeare's England*, 2 Vol, London, 1926, p. 118.
3. H.N. Dasgupta, *The Indian Stage*, Vol. IV, p. 196.
4. Norman Marshall, *Shakespeare Abroad in Talking of Shakespeare*, ed. John Garrett, pp. 91-110
5. Bhartendu Harishchandra: "Bartendu Natakvali, part-II, Parishishtha, Natak" ed. Brijratnadas, p. 416.
6. Badrinath Bhatt: "Durgavati" 1926, pp. 9-12.
7. Shrinivas Das: "Randhir and Prem Mohini" pub. By Hindi Sahitya Samvardhni Sabha, Calcutta, 1915.
8. J.P. Sharma, *Prasad Ke Natakon Ka Shastriya Adhyayan*, p. 55.
9. A. Nicholl, *The English Theatre.* London, 1936, p. 29.
10. C.J. Sission, i "Shakespeare in India," ii "The theatre and companies," articles in *A Companion to Shakespeare Studies* ed. H. Granville Barker and G.B. Harrison, p. 35.
11. Jagdish Prasad Mishra, "Shakespeare impact on Hindi Literature," Munshiram Manoharlal, New Delhi, 1970.
12. Syed Abdul Latif, *The Influence of English Literature on Urdu Literature*, 1924, p. 95.
13. R.W. Fraser, *A Literary History of India*, p. 20.

14. R.K. Yagnik, *The Indian Theatre*, pp. 52-57.
15. Chatterjee, 1980.
16. William Shakespeare, *Romeo and Juliet.* Cambridge University Press, 1997.
17. V.N. Mishra, *Western Influences in Hindi Drama*, p. 86.
18. Jai Shankar Prasad, *Ajatshatru* Bharti Bhandar Leader Press, Prayag, 1957.
19. William Shakespeare, *King Lear*, Cambridge University Press, 1999.
20. William Shakespeare, "Sonnet," ed. G. Blakemore Evans. Cambridge University Press, 1997.
21. Bhikhari Thakur, *Rachnawali*, Bihari Rashtra Bhasha Parishad, 2005.
22. *Smarika*, Bhojpuri Magazine pub. from Bhikhari Thakur Samajik Shodh Sansthan, Arrah, Bihar.

Shakespeare in Indian Theatres

BHASKAR ROY BARMAN
Agartala

Before we deal with how Shakespeare has permeated Indian theatre, let us inform ourselves how Shakespeare's characters have been metamorphosed over the centuries, which shows that they have transcended the barriers of time and place.

The following snippet comes out from the interview given to John O'Connor, author of *Shakespearean After lives* by the actress Sinead Cusack on 7 February 2003:

> In answer to a question asked by the author says the actress: 'On poetry well every level and in every area of society—be it in literature, be it in advertising, be it on a sauce bottle, be it on whatever—you find Shakespeare. And used, I mean, in such a constant and pervasive way that it's astonishing. And the expectation is that people will immediately be able to identify something because of that Shakespearean reference.'
>
> The author puts in: 'You can show a young man in black holding a skull. . .'
>
> Says the actress: 'And everybody knows it's Hamlet! Now that's astonishing! I love it!' (Introduction: 1).

The snippet quoted above attests how Shakespearean influence has continued well into the twenty-first century and his characters still exist, metamorphosed, in different incarnations so much so that their presentation on the stage won't take the audience back to the Shakespearean times. Even outside of England many of Shakespearean characters, particularly Romeo and Juliet, have got incarnated in different characters in different contexts and different situations and speaking different languages.

I myself once savoured a taste of the incarnating of Romeo and Juliet in a Bengali-language play. I can't recollect the title of the play. I myself directed the play written by a well-known playwright presented at an annual function of a school at which I worked as a teacher at Khowai, a sub-division of a tiny state, Tripura in which I am still living. The story of Shakespeare's play *Romeo and Juliet* was transplanted into the Bengali play set in the situation peculiar to Bengal and Romeo and Juliet got incarnated into Bengali names. The play owed its success to the audience because of the romantic appeal.

The romantic approach to Shakespeare's characters persisted well into the twentieth century and still continues into the twenty-first century. But it was subjected to an attack in 1933, as John O'Connor tells us (2005: 5), by L.C. Knights in an essay satirically entitled 'How many Children Had Lady Macbeth?,' his argument being that 'to conceive of Shakespeare's characters as thought they were real people was,' in the words of John O'Connor, "to be guilty of misunderstanding Shakespeare's art , an art which concerns itself with the creation of "dramatic poems"' (7-8). Even though critical theory has moved a long way since the 1930s, a consensus view that still holds sway upon academics is that 'it is both naïve and wrong to think of Shakespeare's character as though they were anything very much more than the sum-total of the words on the page, literary products of "social energy" which circulated in Early Modern era in which Shakespeare lived and worked.' (6)

This view holds good with scholars, but the real problem that has cropped up around this view is related to the fact that the great variety of theatre-going and movie-watching public resolutely subscribe to this view and they won't be got round to this view because 'they have seen Derek Jacobi's Prospero or

Sinead Cusack's Cleopatra or Claire Danes's Juloet' and they cannot be convinced that 'they haven't seen a version of reality which helps them make sense of their own existences.' (6)

Referring to the particular question of Lady Macbeth's children, John O'Connor, quoting Harriet Walter (reference his book *Actors on Shakespeare: Macbeth*, published 2002 by Faber and Faber; 27) says 'Every production has to find a solution. Scholars' concerns lie elsewhere,' tries to elucidate it:

> we, the audience, are an essential part of that production. Finding a solution is as crucial to us as it is to the actor. We collaborate with her, endorsing her conviction that, having in a very real sense 'become' Lady Macbeth, the actor's flesh and blood reality is passed on to the character. We know intellectually that Harriet Walter isn't actually Shakespeare's Scottish Queen. But it's a knowledge we happily subdue as part of our contract with the actor and the production of which she's a part. It's an important manifestation of what the poet Coleridge famously termed 'a willing suspension of disbelief'. (6-7).

It is not so easy a matter to define what a Shakespearian character is and to agree upon the ways in which we find it proper to speak. The difficulty in defining becomes complicated owing to the fact that Shakespeare himself did not offer a consistent view of what a character was. John O'Connor seeks to explain this point elucidated by director Andrian Noble who he interviewed on 2 June 2003 in London Haymarker Theatre. I reproduce below Noble's response to O'Connor's question as concerns this point:

> Shakespeare's attitude towards character shifted and changed during the course of his life, I would say. If you look at his approach to his character in, let's say, the Henry VI plays, pretty early stuff, almost everybody speaks in verse. Almost everybody's thoughts are roughly iambic, which means . . . that almost all the characters have a very strong pulse in the language. The same is true of Titus Andronicus, Richard III, all those early plays. And you could say therefore that maybe they're all similar. Because

> whether it's the Duke of York coming on or Queen Margaret coming on or Clarence coming on, they all think through to the end of the line . . . (p. 9)

The inconsistency on the part of Shakespeare in portrayal of characters helps us to universalize and eternalize his characters, and their traits can be easily fitted into any other character even in modern plays written in English or in any other language, performed in England or at any other place outside England. I would rather elaborate upon this point.

Shakespeare has made his characters unstable and inconsistent because they can be interpreted in different ways to cater to the needs of time and place and particularly because they effectuate different functions at different stages in the dramatist's career. This inconsistency, this unstableness of his plays bestows upon his plays the universality they enjoy.

Before entering into the second section of this article I should like to reproduce below via 'Different Shakespeare: The Bard in Colonial/.Postcolonial India' by Jyotsna Sinha (2009: A: 77) a portion of Carlyle's Lecture entitled 'The Hero as Poet: Dante; Shakespeare', delivered on 12 May 1840, which testifies to the timeless popularity of Shakespeare:

> Consider if they asked us, 'Will you give up your Indian Empire or Shakespeare, you English: never have had any Indian Empire or never have had any Shakespeare? Really it were a grave question. Official persons will answer doubtless in official language, but we, for our part, too, should we not be forced to answer: Indian Empire or no Indian Empire we cannot do without Shakespeare. Indian Empire will go at any rate, some day; but this Shakespeare does not go, he lasts for ever with us, this is the famous comment, as is Shakespeare's fellow playwright Ben Jonson's: Shakespeare's plays are 'not for an age, but for all time.'

Now I switch over to talking about how Shakespeare made inroads into Indian theatres, as the title itself suggests.

One of the most influential and controversial recent debates gravitates towards the relations of dependency and opposition between postcolonial writing and dominant Western forms of textuality. Ashcroft et al in their book *The Empire Writes Back* (1989) treat us to a tit-bit of the argument by saying that 'the act of writing the texts of any kind in postmodern areas is subject to the political imagination, and social control involved in the relationship between colonizers and colonized' (29).

In postcolonial Anglophone literatures, counterdiscursive texts are disposed to clump together particularly round three works that mapped out the psychohistory of colonialism from the early modern down to the modern period. The works referred to are: Shakespeare's *The Tempest* (1611), Daniel Defoe's *Robinson Crusoe* (1719) and Joseph Conrad's *The Heart of Darkness* (1902). And they are characterized as 'paradigmatic colonial texts' and 'classic fictions of the colonial encounter,' unfolding in essence the process of domination, exploitation and brutalization that points to Europe's colonization of the orient.

Leaving aside the theoretical aspect of the three works mentioned, we cannot bring ourselves to deny the truth that the concept of canonical counterdiscourse gives unto us a partial view of postcolonial textual and cultural politics. It is worth noting in this context that the emphasis placed on 'writing back' is also steered on an inordinate significance bestowed upon the continued relationship of the postcolonial periphery to the imperial centre via the medium of European languages, mainly English, suffice it to say, and marginalizes those forms of writing and performances that happen to be non-European and not concerned primarily with the colonial experience.

The scope of this article does not permit elaborate discussion of this concept. Now let us pass on to Indian theatre as a multilingual field of performance which poses a resistance to the Eurocentric, hierarchical and textually motivated model of literary relations proffered by the concept of canonical counterdiscourse, its subject to substantial modification in order to be attuned to actual textual and performative functions of appropriation. The textual field of theatre in India is characterized by a blend of classical, premodern, modern and contemporary interests, both Western and non-Western. The multitudinous assimilation of Western and non-Western drama as well had contributed to diversifying and consolidating, at the same time, an emergent theatrical culture by adopting a process of introducing into it non-indigenous narratives and textual practices. It is because Indian playwrights are usually prone to write the canonical texts, as they regard such writing as legitimate exercise of authorship.

Now let us pass on to the dramatic movement in India to clear the way for Shakespearean plays to intrude into Indian theatres.

William Jones announced in the preface to his translation of Kalidasa's Sanskrit drama *Shakuntala* (qtd. Basudha Dalmia) the national drama of the Hindus to the occident, Basudha quoted him as saying in the preface, 'Dramatic poetry must have been immemorially ancient in the ancient empire. . . . The play of *Shakuntala* must have been very popular when it was first represented; for the Indian empire was then in full vigour, and the national vanity must have been highly flattered by the magnificent introduction of those kings and heroes in whom the Hindus gloried; the scenery must have been splendid and beautiful; and there is good reason to believe, that court in Avanti is equal in brilliancy during the reign of Vikramaditya, to that of any monarch in any age or country.' (28).

William Jones, who had been the first to identify the genius of Shakespeare, conceived the ideas of monolith which he termed Hindu theatre. His ideas were based on indigenous Brahminical sources rather than on his own observation of the performative traditions which abounded in that region.

It is worth-mentioning in this connection another important orientalist, Horace Hayman Wilson, who introduced the grandeur of the Indian drama to the Western world by translating into English select specimens of the Indian Theatre and incorporated them into a book referenced below. He showed concern with the Indian drama forty years after William Jones. His enthusiasm, though circumspect and qualified in some ways, corroborated the national status of the Indian drama. He held the opinion that Indian theatre did not confine itself to depicting the glories of the Indian empire; as befits the dramatic literature of every nation, it furnished examples of dramas of domestic and heroic life and examples as well of original invention and legendary tradition. In the introduction to his book, Horace Hayman Wilson says, as quoted by Vaudha Dalmia on page 30, 'The theatrical representation of modern Europe, however, diversified by national features, are legitimate offspring of the classical drama.' By 'classical' is obviously meant ancient Greek drama. But the Indian theatre had its own origin and belonged to a division which modern critics had termed romantic, as opposed to the 'classical.'

The beginnings of modern theatre can be traced to the colonial encounter that resulted in the influence of Western and European plays on local theatrical traditions. The British form permeated the cultural life of Bengal as early as 1757 when Bengal came under the rule of East India Company and many important and prominent playhouses proliferated and thrived under the direct patronage of colonial officials. Prominent among them were the Calcutta Theatre built in 1775, Chowringhee Theatre built in 1813 and Sans Souci Theatre opened in 1839. English theatres, starting, as they did, in 1775 when the Calcutta Theatre or the New Playhouse operated under the direct patronage of Warren Hastings and continued well into the nineteenth century performed no mean number of plays just in order to amuse and occupy largely British audience of sahibs and memsahibs. Initially restricted to the sahibs and memsahibs, the theatrical activity escalated. Local literati and men of wealth, enthused by the success of the plays staged in these playhouses, resorted to financing and staging European plays at local theatres, schools and on college stages. This theatrical activity led to the emergence by the late nineteenth century of a stream of urban drama and the emergence owed itself to the influence of Anglo-European traditions. But there is no denying the fact that it remained the least commended aesthetic form as compared to the novel and poetry. Despite the low profile of the drama, theatre had developed by the late nineteenth century into a broad-based entertainment in urban centres such as Calcutta, Madras and Bombay and attracted larger middle class audience.

Owing to the simultaneous intensification of an anti-colonial movement that suffused the theatrical scenes with ideas, modern theatre came to be characterized by several paradoxes. According to many theatre critics in Bengal, Partha Chatterjee being one of them, these paradoxes resulted from the commingling of two models that permeated the dramatic literature of Bengal in the middle of the nineteenth century: one of the models being the modern European drama which has found a strong foothold by this time, and the other being the Sanskrit drama which was restored to a reputation of classical excellence, thanks to the praises heaped upon it by the orientalist scholars from Europe.

Surprisingly, the dramatic histories I have alluded to in this article make no mention of Balshnav Charan Adya who is supposed to have been the first to perform the role of a Shakespearean character, Othello in a production at the Sans Souci Theatre, the famous English playhouse in Calcutta at a time when Calcutta turned out to be the intellectual and political centre of colonial presence. Reference to this singular incidence by Jyotsna Sinha has reminded me of my having read of this contribution quoted by Kiranmoy Raha in his book *Bengali Theatre* published by National Book Trust, India in 1988.

It deserves to be mentioned in this context that some members of the audience who had seen the role of Othello performed by a 'nigger' and others who had read the report in the *Calcutta Star* reacted to the event. Their objection was voiced in a letter published in a contemporary issue of *Calcutta Star* that mentions the actor as 'real unpainted Othello'.

The question pertinent to this context pertains to the patronizing of the performances of Shakespearean works and those of other canonized works in India. The reproductions of Shakespeare's works and works of other canonized writers were connected with a political strategy of introducing them into Indian English culture. Thanks to the incursion of the English culture through the presentation of Shakespearean and other plays, there occurred a spurt of staging indigenous performances of the plays which produced, vernacular Shakespeares, conciliated by the heterogeneous commingling of race, language and native language.

In course of time Shakespeare acquired a strong foothold through the love of the theatre and that of Shakespeare, first developed among the English community and later passed on to its Indian emulators. The Calcutta Theatre, established in 1775 boosted the trend of performing Shakespearean plays one after another without cease. Jyotsna Sinha writes: 'The repertoire of plays performed at this theatre included *Hamlet*, *Richard III*, *The School for Scandal* and a medley of lesser-known plays such as *The Comedy of Beaux Stratagem* and *She Would and Would Not* and inform us that most theatre historians tell us that a certain Mr. Bernad Massing got sent out to Calcutta by David Garrick to supervise the Calcutta Theatre. The model for the playhouse in the colonies clearly 'came from the theatrical arrangements and architecture of Covent Garden, Drury Lane etc. In fact one account suggests that David Garrick sent a number of scenes painted under his direction for the theatre (81).

The Chowringhee, opened in 1813, did not lag behind in boosting the spree of performing Shakespearean plays, such as *Henry IV* on 23 January 1814, *Richard III* on 25 August 1815, and *The Merry Wives of Windsor* on 25 September 1918.

The Sans Souci, another English theatre was inaugurated on 21 August 1839. It was established in the year that witnessed the devastation by fire of the Chowringhee theatre, and was moved to a bigger building in 1841. Mrs. Esther Leach, a prominent actress attached to the Chowringhee theatre, shifted her allegiance to the Sans Siouci and had a few artists brought down from London.

Mr. James Vining, who had acquired proficiency in acting in Drury Lane and Covent Garden, utilized the proficiency in presenting some performances at the Sans Souci. He appeared in Shakespeare's *The Merchant of Venice* staged on 2 November 1843 with Mrs. Esther Leach, playing Shylock. A certain Mrs. Deacle played Portia. It is a historical truth that the prominence Mr. James Vining acquired by giving performances at the Sans Souci was surpassed by that native gentleman Baishnav Charan Adya, a Bengali youth who played Othello with Mrs. Abderson, the daughter of Mrs. Esther Leach.

The gradual involvement of Bengali aristocrats educated in English literature and language with the Calcutta theatres was linked to the official policy of popularizing in India English literature and language. To popularize English language and literature in India was urgently felt essential in order to consolidate the colonial presence in India. The impulse that worked towards educating the native elite class was based on the premise that the native people were required to be co-opted in order to use them as a conduit to channel Western thought and ideas into the country they had colonized.

It is not difficult in the context of the nineteenth century Calcutta to perceive the significance of why the empire had invested in Shakespeare's works both as literary and dramatic texts. Historical evidence shows how Indians loved Shakespeare and this colonial legacy handed over to Indians has continued with undiminishing vigour into postcolonial discourse in India. It is not at all difficult to imagine how fondly the elite Bengalis cherished this legacy at that time.

By the elite Bengalis are meant roughly lawyers, doctors, writers, educationists, and in course of time, people of other vocations found themselves imbibed with many-sided interests, thanks to their dip into the flow of English literature and language into India, one of their interests being in English drama. They admired the drama and aspired to copy it, swayed away by their enthusiasm to create a Bengali stage. The history of Bengali theatres in Calcutta started at that time. It points both to admiration for and ambivalence towards English plays, notably Shakespeare's. While Shakespearean plays were produced in the early nineteenth century in response to the desire to imitate, almost blindly, the English culture, in course of time the texture of them sort of manipulated to cater to the needs of the indigenous audiences.

There was no theatrical activity worth-mentioning here on the Bengali stage from 1835 to 1853 except for a lavish Bengali production entitled *Vidya Sundar* which ran for three years from 1833 to 1835. David Clinger, a teacher at the David Hare Academy, associated with the Sans Souci Theatre, directed *The Merchant of Venice* staged on 16 and 24 February 1853 with the students of the Academy acting in it, to pave the way for the students of the Oriental Seminary in North Calcutta to get involved in dramatic performances. Enthused by the success of the performance, the students and ex-students of the Seminary set up a theatre named Oriental Theatre on 7 April 1853 by raising subscriptions, for staging Shakespearean plays. A good number of Shakespearean plays were staged at the Oriental Theatre for a number of years. The evidence available suggests an awareness on the part of those involved in the theatrical performance under the aegis of Oriental Theatre of the impact on them of the theatre and of the culture of the hybrid nature of this venture.

It should be noted that staging in 1957 of the first Bengali drama at a private theatre heralded the end of the period of a direct cultural subservience to English theatrical models. But most of Shakespearean plays got translated or adapted for the Bengali-language plays and a number of them were performed on the public stage from 1874 to 1920. We cannot—can we?—measure the influence of Shakespeare by the number of plays performed but we can do so by examining his influence that permeated the writing of the budding playwrights of Bengal. It is Shakespeare who tutored the budding playwrights of Bengal through his plays produced in Bengal on the concept of tragedy, the meaning of conflict and particularly on how to turn the drama into a dramatic expression of life in its moment of conflict, crisis and catastrophe.

There was a long gap after 1920 until the late 1940s when Shakespeare was revived on the Bengali stage. Beginning in the early 1930s Bengali theatres gradually broadened its audience who were clamouring for the social and political realities of the Indian masses to be shown on the stage. When Shakespearean plays were revived around 1948 on the Bengali stage, the production smacked of the influence of contemporary social realities. But the undeniable truth is that Shakespeare has not disappeared and will not disappear from the theatrical arena. He lurks incognito behind every dramatic writing, as is evident in the affirmation in a report on a discussion on 'Why Read Shakespeare?' held on 20 January 1988 at the University of Delhi, published in 'Bulletin of Shakespeare Society of India, April 1988 [qtd. Jyotsna Sinha (2009:A: 93)]:

we read Shakespeare because he transcends all ages, nations and cultures, and can, therefore be assimilated into any age, nation or culture. He deals with human beings, their sentiment and feelings, and since these do not change in any real sense, Shakespeare's appeal is timeless and universal. Further the issues he raises, the clash of values, he depicts, are relevant to us and to our situation.

Bibliography

Lal, Ananda, ed. (2009), *Theatres of India: A Concise Companion;* Oxford University Press, New Delhi.

Bhatia, Nandi, ed. (2009), *Modern Indian Theatre*; Oxford University Press, New Delhi.

Dhanwadker, Aparna Bhargava (2006), *Theatres of Independence* (2006); Oxford University Press, New Delhi.

O'Connor, John (2005), *Shakespearean Afterlives*; Icon Books, Cambridge, U.K.

Dalmia Basudha (2006), *The Politics of Modern Indian Drama*; Oxford University Press, New Delhi.

Ashcroft, Bill, Gareth, Griffiths and Helen Tiffin (1989), *The Empire Writes Back*: *Theory and Practice in Postcolonial Literatures*; Routledge, London.

A Comparative Study of *Auchitya* Theory with Special Reference to Shakespeare's Plays: *Othello* and *Macbeth*

RAKHI JAIN
Bharati College, University of Delhi

A systematic exposition of the principles of poetics in India began with Bharat's *Natyashastra* though its traces started peeping through the earliest known works in Sanskrit like Vedas and Puranas. Similarly, literary criticism in the west may be traced back to the earliest Homeric hymns, while a systematic presentation of its underlying tenets is to be seen in the writings of Plato and Aristotle. Thus, literary criticism has been developing for around two thousand years simultaneously at both the places. After going through a comparative study of both the traditions, we come to know that all the literary critics and artists, whether Indian or western, claim one element indispensable underlying all the theories and that is Auchitya or Propriety.

In fact, the concept of propriety has loomed large in the speculation of Indian Acharyas over ages and it has come out in two-fold ways, first, harmony with social sanction and second, harmony with artistic expression. Right from the ancient time, the behaviour which is based on Auchitya or propriety is viable and that which is inconsistent with it, is not approved by society. In a way, the society consists of the group of behaviours. The relationship between parents and children, teacher and disciple, brother and sister, wife and husband and man and man is based on 'Auchitya'. Even in the orbit, the planets, the stars, the Sun and the Moon move in consonance with one another if they drift away from a particular system and order, the destruction is inevitable.

As 'Auchitya' is the inseparable part of our daily life, so is it in the sphere of art and literature. Only that critic who understands well what is proper and what is improper can succeed in his field. The person who lacks the sense of propriety can neither be a writer nor a critic. While dealing with different elements of drama, Bharat deals elaborately with dress and make-up which, he says must be appropriate to the mood and sentiments. Not only this but language and dress should be appropriate to the character. "The dress must be appropriate to the age, the action to the dress, dialogue to the action and the acting to dialogue" (Pathak: 63: 1967)[1].

Not only Bharat but other great Indian critics like Bhamah, Dandi, Anand Vardhan, Abhinav Gupt and all consider Auchitya as much inevitable as the absence of which can make the edifice of all the theories Rasa, Dhvani, Alankar, Vakrokti topple down. "Indian Poetics never recognized propriety as an end in itself or a virtue to be cultivated for its own sake. . . . It was regarded as sine qua non of all literary theories, something without which no theory, however, competent, could succeed" (Kushwaha: 101: 1988). While dealing with Alankaras, Bhamah says that certain demerits cease to be demerits under certain circumstances and merits become demerits in inappropriate situations. As repetition is a flaw in expression but turns out to be an effective way of expression in fear, sorrow, jealousy, joy and wonder. King Yashoverman of Kanauj for the first time used this word 'Auchitya' in his prologue to *Ramabhyudaya*.

He talks of two kinds of Auchitya. First, speech should be according to nature and level of the character and second, rasa should be developed in a proper place according to the sentiments of a character (Yashovarma, Srangar Prakash, Part

II).[2] Anandvardhan has given it the most important place by relating it to Rasa which is the soul of poetry. He is of the view that "except impropriety, there is no other cause for the abatement of the relish of poetry. A composition containing the well known propriety is the very secret of flavour (Rudrata, Kavyalankara)."[3] In his work 'Locana', Anandvardhan comments on three elements of poetry viz., Rasa, Dhvani and Auchitya.

Abhinav Gupt points out one thing, that is, 'Abhasa' which is the result of Anauchitya. If a Kavya does not have Auchitya it is 'Kavyabhasa', if Rasa does not have Auchitya, it is 'rasa bhasa', like this there is 'Alankarabhasa' if Auchitya is not found in Alankara. In fact, critics of the time were aware of two things especially Auchitya and Dhvani. Mahim Bhatt, who propounds the theory of Dhvani, regards Auchitya as indispensable. According to him there can be no opposition to it, he fights only for Dhvani. Whatever flaws are hindrance to Rasa, Mahim Bhatt calls them by one name, Anauchitya, that is, the absence of appropriateness.

However, it got its place among the school of thoughts with the hands of Kshemendra of eleventh century who wrote a full-length treatise: *Auchitya Vichara Charcha*. According to him, all the constituents of Auchitya are like quintessence of Kavya. In brief, just as the soul pervades the whole human body, the Auchitya element is present in every article and particle of poetry and just as by striking at the vital point of body, they should leave the body. Similarly, if there is any kind of blow at vital point of poetry, the auchitya leaves the poetry, that is, the poetry becomes lifeless (Jha: 1982).[4]

As Kshemendra in India gave rise to a whole school of critical thinking based on the notion of Auchitya, similarly, Aristotle, Horace, Longinus in west, gave due consideration to this notion. As Bharat insists that playwrights and producers should take the people as their authority, in the same way

Aristotle suggests the poet should remember to put the actual scenes as far as possible before his eyes. "In this way, seeing everything with the vividness of an eye-witness as it were, he will devise what is appropriate and be likely to overlook incongruity (Aristotle, *On the Art of Poetry*).

The description of Propriety in western criticism is not made in such a way as can establish a full-fledged principle, but its concept has been recognized there also in one or the other form. It has been expressed through various terms such as conformity, appropriateness, fitness, propriety, decorum, harmony, congruity, suitability, coincidence, aptness, correctness etc. The definition is also the same. According to Kshemendra, "The thing which is proper to which and its expression is Auchitya or Propriety." The same definition has been given by westerners: "Conformity of related things to each other; conformity in relation to some recognized ideal for such relation, coincidence in matters of relatedness, of what is with what ought to be" (Joseph and Shipley, *Dictionary of World Literature*: 160).

Almost every great western critic has accepted its importance and talked about it as Aristotle, Horace, Longinus, Pope, Dr. Johnson, Dryden, Wordworth, Coleridge, T.S. Eliot, I.A. Richards, to name a few.

In the second book, *Rhetorics*, Aristotle expresses his views about the other elements of poetry such as figure of speech etc. He says that the main source of decorating a proper piece is the use of metaphor but it should be in conformity with the subject. Thus, he emphasizes upon the Auchitya of Alankar of Kshemendra. He further says, "If a tender subject is expressed in harsh language or a harsh subject in tender language there is a certain loss of persuasiveness (Aristotle, *Rhetorics*). All the sources of sublimity, in *On the Sublime* by Longinus, are based on propriety; without propriety the literary piece does not remain sublime. Commenting upon the defects that mitigate sublimity he says: "Now even in tragedy, which by its very nature is majestic and admits of some bombast, misplaced timidity is unpardonable; still less, I think would it be appropriate to factual narration." (Longinus, *On the Sublime*)

The thing which Anandvardhan says about the propriety of figure of speech is stated in the same way by Longinus. According to Anandvardhan only that figure of speech creates charm which is not imposed and laboured but arises from the occasion and the main thought. Longinus too stresses upon the same, "thus a rhetorical figure would appear to be most effective when the fact that it is a figure, is not apparent" (Longinus, *On the Sublime*). These figures of speech should be appropriate to the contest at the same time lest it would mar the beauty of poetry.

Horace through *Ars Poetica* has advised three things to poets: Follow the Greek Ideals, save the form of character and follow the concept of propriety. In respect of third one he comes closer to Acharya Bharat. He further comments upon the art of acting and in it he shows the importance of propriety at uttermost. As Anandvardhan and Kshemendra say that without propriety there will be no effect of acting, Horace says that if the speech is out of harmony with the feeling, it will arouse only laughter, "Pathetic language is appropriate to the fact of sorrow and violent language to the face of anger; a sportive diction goes with merry looks, and a serious with grave looks" (Horace, *Art of Poetry*)

Not only Greek philosophers but in England in the eighteenth century, writers are much concerned about decorum. In his *Essay on Criticism*, Alexander Pope emphasizes upon the propriety of word or phrase. The words should be suggestive in Nature:

> It is not enough no harshness gives offence
> The sound must seem an Echo to the sense;
> soft is the strain when Zephyr gently blows;
> And the smooth stream in smoother numbers flows;

But when long surges lash the sounding shore.

The hoarse, rough verse should like the torrent roar. (Alexander Pope, *An Essay on Criticism*)

Pope here means to say that there should be a harmony between the descriptive thing and the words, that is, there should be propriety of words. In eighteenth century the poets were the followers of system and system in other words can be called propriety. Like Horace, John Dryden also thinks that there should be a particular genre as "rhyme which you acknowledge to be proper to epic poesy, cannot equally be proper to dramatic. (John Dryden, *An Essay on Dramatic Poesy*)

In the "Preface to Shakespeare" by Dr. Johnson, we find the overtones of propriety at many places. For him, propriety can make even vulgar things readable, "those who wish for distinction forsake the vulgar, when vulgar is right; but there is a conversation above grossness and below refinement, where propriety resides." (*Preface to Shakespeare*) Among romantics Wordsworth is of the view that if a man is writing on humble and rustic life he should choose that very language "because in that condition of life our elementary feelings cooperate in a state of greater simplicity." (*Preface to Lyrical Ballads*) Wordsworth suggests choosing the language proper to subject matter and character.

In modern times when T.S. Eliot says that there should be "association of sensibility" and when I.A. Richards talks of two uses of language—emotive and scientific, they talk about propriety in one form or the other. Richards regards emotive use to be proper for poetry. He in this way, accepts Rasa-Auchitya of Kshemendra. Hence, different western critics have accepted and talked about different kinds of Auchitya of Kshemendra, one of the most important elements in Indian Poetics.

Now Shakespeare is no more known as a colonized writer though he was introduced by missionaries in some parts of India in early eighteenth century. It was with the opening of institutions like the Hindu College in Calcutta in 1817 that the systematic study of English literature began and Shakespeare was enshrined in classroom. So after covering such a long journey he no more remains a stranger to Indian sensibility. As a Shakespeare student, I was surprised to find all the twenty-seven kinds of Auchitya theory in his plays. I am going to concentrate myself only on one kind Kalochit, that is, propriety of time in two of his plays: *Othello* and *Macbeth.* In all his plays, Shakespeare creates an atmosphere and presents his characters and image and according to the time he chooses for the action of the play.

Othello is the play of modern times. The plot of Othello has been borrowed from the seventh novel, *The Moor of Venice* written by Giraldi Cinthio, a Silican novelist. In that novel also there is an attack of Turks upon Cyprus and Shakespeare has also shown the same events. If we consult History, we find that though Othello, the hero, is not a historical figure but the Turkish attack on Cyprus is a historical event. For centuries together Venice was the safeguard of the west against the attacks of the mighty Turks. In 1487, the island of Cyprus came to Venice from the Turks by right of conquest. Afterwards, the Turks tried to regain it, it was taken by them during the reign of their glorious kind Salim II about the year 1570. Thus, since the story of Othello took place in the late sixteenth century, we can say that this play belongs to modern age. After the renaissance by virtue of scientific discoveries, people had shed off most of their superstitions and their faith in witches and ghosts, specially the people in Europe were quite modern in their approaches. They had no blind faith in anything. However, people belonging to Africa did not totally come out of their superstitions. We find the same in this play; we do not find any character who is superstitious except Othello who is often described a native of different creed, culture and colour. The description in the play shows him to be an African or a negro and by that time the Africans were not educated enough to liberate themselves from Orthodoxies. We do not find any ghost or witch in the play. Even when Desdemona has the premonition of her death, nobody mentions it as a bad omen. Desdemona is not worried about the handkerchief till Othello is angry with her at the loss of it. She never mentions anywhere that she is worried about the handkerchief because it has some superstition connected with it, as Othello tells her. She wants to have it back merely because it is the first love-token given to her by Othello. She never relates it to any story or any omen, ill or bad. On the other hand, Othello related the loss of handkerchief to witchcraft:

> The handkerchief
> Did an Egyptian to my mother give,
> She was a charmer and could almost read
> The thoughts of people. She told her, while she kept it,
> 'Twould make her amiable and subdue my father
> Entirely to her love; but if she lost it
> Or made a gift of it, my father's eye
> Should hold her loathed. . .
> To lose it or give it away were such perdition.
> As nothing else could match. (*Othello*, III, iv, 57-70)

Thus Shakespeare preserves the propriety of time.

The propriety of time can also be seen in the treatment of the different sections of the day. Night is associated with the dark and malicious actions as it is black, while morning gives life to all natural elements and freshens them. So it is associated with triumph and happiness. Hence, events which leave some brutal effect upon one or the other characters happen only in the darkness of night. The play opens late at night when Brabantio feels heartbroken at the elopement of his daughter with a man of different creed, caste, culture and colour. At this time of night, Iago speaks ill of Othello and pours out all the malicious intentions into the ears of Roderigo. During the same night we listen to the attack of Turks upon Cyprus. It is again in the night when Othello and Desdemona go to bed for the first time for the consummation of their marriage which will soon be turned into disaster. It is again the night when Cassio is dismissed as a result of the loss of temper.

As the day breaks, we listen to the melodious sound of music played by musicians brought by Cassio and his followers. In the morning, Cassio is not so disheartened as he was in the night. With the breaking of the day, he begins his efforts to regain his position. The most chaotic and confusing scene also takes place in the night in which Roderigo is killed by his own accomplice and Cassio's leg is cut. It is a dark night when identities are mistaken and the spirit of evil seems to be stalking the world. Had this scene be shown in the day light, Iago's plan would have failed as in that case Cassio would have easily recognized his enemy. Thus this scene has propriety of time.

The most brutal tragedy that occurs in the play is the murder of a faithful wife by her own husband on the bed and that too takes place at night. The writer describes it clearly, "Desdemona in bed asleep; a light burning" (V, ii) and in such an atmosphere and time enters Othello. Harmonizing with the heart and intention of Othello which is dark and black, Shakespeare shows the time and atmosphere to be equally dark and black. The room is even darker than the outside world hence a light is needed. The stage directions and the style of Shakespeare at this time give the impression that even the light was dimly burning. Thus in this appropriate atmosphere and time, the murder of Desdemona takes place. After the murder, the door is knocked at by Emilia and the light enters into the room in the form of revelation of Iago's villainy. Thus, Shakespeare preserves the propriety of time.

According to the historical facts, the events described in the play *Macbeth* belong to the year 1040. In Scottish history, Duncan was the grandson of Malcolm II and he succeeded his grandfather to the throne of Scotland in 1034 and reigned till 1040. Duncan was the cousin of Macbeth in the sense that Malcolm II had two daughters—Beatrice and Doado. Beatrice's son was Duncan and Doado's was Macbeth. Duncan at once named his son Malcolm Canmore to be his heir, and prince of Cumberland. Macbeth's father was killed in an encounter with Malcolm and therefore Macbeth had a bloody revenge to take against Duncan, the successor of Malcolm. Macbeth's wife was Grouch. The head of her family was murdered by Malcolm; so she also was keen on having a bloody revenge upon Malcolm family and Duncan became the victim. History has it that Macbeth was the trusted general of Duncan, he had defeated a number of Duncan's enemies and ultimately murdered Duncan and succeeded to the throne of Scotland. Thus history proves that the story of Macbeth took place in eleventh century which is known as medieval period.

In medieval times, people were not educated hence they were superstitious and had firm faith in witches and ghosts. Not only the common man but the gentry also was equally superstitious. Thus, Shakespeare introduces witches and ghosts in the play to preserve the propriety of time. The witches have been shown to have the world of their own and the name of their queen is Hecate. Most of the plays written in the medieval period, were full of darkness and melodramatic events. The whole of the play *Macbeth* is brooded over with the darkness which is not of the night only but of the crime also. The loneliness of the blasted heath and the appearance of the witches create an atmosphere of awe and horror. Macbeth wades through the pool of blood killing one after another to secure the throne. Banquo is killed and the most melodramatic scene is the one in which Macduff's innocent wife and little kid are brutally put to death.

Not only the incidents but imagery and repetition of the some words also create the ghastly atmosphere, very typical of medieval times. It seems as if people were bathing in the pool of blood. Macbeth cries out, "I am in blood stepp'd in so far that, should I wade no more" (I, ii, 39-40). In fact the word 'blood' echoes throughout the play. First of all, a bloody man comes to king Duncan to narrate the events of the battlefield. Lady Macbeth and Macbeth have blood-stained hands. The murderer with Banquo's blood on his face appears before the gate of Banquet hall; Macbeth seems to be holding a bloody sceptre in his hand and so on.

To create the medieval environment and to show the propriety of time, most of the crimes have been committed in the darkness of night; the vision of the dagger, the murder of Duncan, the sleep-walking of Lady Macbeth, the dance of the witches in the thick air of the storm and Macbeth's meeting the witches in a lonely place, to name a few. Even the introductory scene of Act II opens in past midnight, black as Macbeth's heart and in that black night, Macbeth has to commit his first crime so that his own eyes may not be able to see his own downfall. The darkness of the night creates a feeling of terror in the hearts of both Macbeth and Lady Macbeth and here lies the spirit of the play.

As people of the time were superstitious so we meet witches and ghosts in the play. Being superstitious, people believe in such witches as can raise storms, lightning and thunder and make the weather foul. They can fly in the air from place to place. They can keep devils and spirits in the form of cats. They can reveal to others things hidden and lost such as they show to Macbeth the long line of Banquo's children as kings of Scotland. The spirits are their masters; they are subject to Hecate who herself is a superior devil. Thus, bloodshed, ghastly scenes, horrible atmosphere pervades throughout the play which is in consonance with the atmosphere of the medieval times and plays written at that time.

Auchitya/Propriety hence is a means to verisimilitude, a device to make a speech or composition convincing and effective. Shakespeare, though four centuries have passed, is still regarded as one of the greatest writers of the world literature and he could attain such a height because he kept this element, that is, Auchitya, in his mind, though unconscious of it.

Works Cited

Quotations of all western critics have been taken from *Literary Criticism: An Anthology, Aristotle to T.S. Eliot*, ed., D.K. Chopra, Lyall, Meerut, 1980.

All the Sanskrit Shlokas have been translated by S.K. De, *History of Sanskrit Poetics*, Calcutta University Press.

Badawi, M.M. *Background to Shakespeare*, London & Basingstoke; Higher and further education Division, Macmillan, 1984.

Chambers, Edmund K., ed., *The Tragedy of Macbeth*, London & Glasgow: Blackie, 1970.

Clemen, Wolfgang, *The Development of Shakespeare's Imagery*, London; Methuen, 1977.

Honigmann, E.A.J., ed., The Arden Shakespeare; *Othello*, 1999.

Kanta, Surya, *Kshemendra Studies*, Poona: Oriental Book Agency, 1966.

Kshemendra, *Auchitya Vichar Charcha*, Acharya Shri Vraj Mohan Jha, ed. Varanasi: Chaukhamba Vidyabhavan, 1982.

Kushwaha, M.S., ed. *Indian Poetics and Western Thought*, Agro Publishing House, Lucknow, 1988.

Mangan, Michael, *A Preface to Shakespeare's Tragedies*, Pearson Education, Delhi, 2003.

Paliwal, Prem Lata, *An Oriental Approach to Shakespearean Tragedy*, Mathura; Rajyashri Prakashan.

Pathak, Chanderhans, *Auchitya, Sampradaya Ka Hindi-Kavya-Shastra par Prahav*, Chowkhamba Vidyabhawan, Varanasi, 1967.

Tiwary, R.S., *A Critical Approach to Classical Indian Poetics, Varanasi: Chaukhamba Oriental*, 1984.